FLIGHT INTO SPACE

THE FACTS, FANCIES AND PHILOSOPHY

FLIGHT IN

THE FACTS, FANCIES

RANDOM HOUSE, NEW YORK

TO SPACE

AND PHILOSOPHY

JONATHAN NORTON LEONARD

contents

FLIGHT INTO SPACE

THE FACTS, FANCIES AND PHILOSOPHY

1

THREE LEVELS

The earth is round and small, and there is little that man does not know about it, but around the earth lies the ocean of space, a highway to other worlds. When will man travel this highway, which leads beyond the stars? Will it be soon, or eventually, or never?

The kids have already "blasted off"; they can buy space suits and one-kid rockets at almost any toy store. The heroes of the comics are fighting bad men on Mars. The subtler heroes of science fiction have pushed their operations beyond the Milky Way. Space has become the wild frontier of the modern imagination. To those who find the earth too well known, too tame, too dull, it offers unbounded adventure. To those who have faith in man and mind, it is a chance for the greatest achievement of the human race since the start of its history.

Not only the kids, storytellers and crackpots have turned their hopes toward space. Serious scientists are devoting their time to the details of space flight and space inhabitation. Astronomers dream about the wonderful things that they could do with unhampered telescopes floating above the earth's atmosphere. Biologists dream of finding and studying strange kinds of life on planets with novel atmospheres. In every great laboratory, every university, every proving ground of aircraft or guided missiles are men who give part of their thinking time to the glittering, many-faceted challenge that stares at them from space.

A lot of this stuff is wishful thinking, juvenile or adult. Some of it is intellectual capering by scholars who like to play difficult games. But below this froth is a solid stratum of fact and probable theory. Man's headlong technical development is moving toward space. For more than ten years now his rockets have soared above the atmosphere. Each year, behind the blackout of military secrecy, they fly a little more surely. If the present rate of progress keeps up, which it may or may not do, manned space flight will be a real possibility.

This book will attempt to separate some of the facts of space flight from some of the theories and fictions. It will take account of three levels. The first concerns the accomplishments and attitudes of the men who design, build and fly modern rockets up to the boundaries of space. This is an exciting subject, and it would be exciting even if it did not have a great objective in its future. It is a difficult subject to deal with because all work on rockets is also work on military guided missiles and is therefore jealously guarded by the world's governments.

The second level is theory. A scientific campaign does not advance with a solid front; it pushes ahead at some points and lags at others. It develops elaborate plans to take enemy strongholds which lie for the present far beyond its reach. It trains its troops to use weapons that have not been constructed or perhaps not even imagined. It is not discouraged by any lack that may be corrected later.

Space enthusiasts like to compare the present period with the era just before Columbus when Europeans were about to vault the Atlantic. The comparison is not exact. Columbus did not know what he would find across the ocean, but he did have ships that would take him there. The space men know a great deal about what lies beyond the atmosphere, but at present they have no effective ships. They are like a Columbus who can see from the mountains of Spain the continents of North and South America, but who has only a rowboat to carry him across the Atlantic.

While waiting for their space rowboats to develop into space caravels, the space men have elaborated an enormous body of theory to guide their future campaigns. Some of it is exact, and needs no further improvement. Other parts are still soft but are gaining substance continually. Other parts are only misty outlines waiting for information that still lies beyond man's reach. This book will examine some of these theories and try to assay their content of fact.

The third level is imagination, the very mixed bag of solemn or playful dreaming that may be called space fiction. Much of it is worthless, wild-west stuff transferred for the sake of modernity to the surfaces of distant or nonexistent planets. But some of it has a kind of vision, and its popularity, which increases continuously, is proof that space flight has become one of man's great dreams.

Space fiction is the modern equivalent of the travelers' tales that entertained Europeans before they could send their coast-bound ships beyond the encircling ocean. In those days travelers returned from their dangerous journeys, which were often imaginary journeys, with stories of men who stood on one leg or who had heads like dogs. Or tales of birds that could carry off full-grown oxen. Or of whirlpools in the sea, or of happy races of men who lived without pain or hunger. Such tales were a lure that drew real travelers into the real unknown. In the same way space fiction now leads modern men to think about the mysteries, perils and marvels that surround the earth.

Behind the techniques and projects of space flight lies the haunting and rather frightening thought that man's move into space may be the next great step that has been assigned to evolving life. Man is new on the planet Earth, and civilized man who co-operates socially and accumulates knowledge has existed for only a hair-thin sliver of geological time. Scientific man is still newer, and fully technological man has been functioning in only a few places for less than a century.

But already man has changed the appearance of his planet. Forests and prairies have turned into plowed lands. Deserts have turned green. Man's industrial fires and engine exhausts are speeding up the carbon cycle, on which all plant and animal life depends. The night glow of man's cities and the flash of his atom bombs are conspicuous far out in space.

The planet Earth is stirring. Man's intelligence has already become a geological force. Barring catastrophes and self-destruction, man may yet expand beyond the boundaries of the earth. Then life, which began in the sea and pioneered the hostile land, may move into even more difficult space and thrive there enormously, as it throve on the land. When this happens, man's intelligence will have become an astronomical force.

There is much overlapping among the levels of space flight. The most solid achievements of the practical rocket men have an unreal quality that makes them hard to believe even when witnessed direct. And the wildest theories and fancies of the space-travel enthusiasts often contain a trace of cold reality. It is hard to judge at this fast-changing stage which apparent facts are fancies, and which apparent fancies are really embryonic facts.

To make sure of one set of dreamlike facts, let us start with White Sands Proving Ground, New Mexico, that extremely romantic place where actual rockets with tails of flame fly into the blue sky.

2

SACRIFICE AT WHITE SANDS

A rocket shoot at White Sands Proving Ground is more than interesting, more than beautiful, more than exciting. It is inspiring in a way that is equaled by few sights on earth.

Behind the austere buildings of the military post rise the spectacular Organ Mountains with a fringe of dark pine trees climbing to their highest ridges. An uninhabited wilderness presses from all sides upon this isolated outpost of technological man. Jack rabbits bounce among the cactus and yucca. Deer dance down from the mountains at night to browse on the post's garbage, and sometimes mountain lions follow to browse on the deer.

In front, for forty miles, sweeps the gray-green desert

of the Tularosa Basin. Dust devils swirl across it like yellow tornadoes, and sometimes great sandstorms blot out the sun. But much of the time the air is as clear as a vacuum, showing a rim of distant mountains around the flat desert floor. A person standing in the center beyond where the rockets fly can easily imagine himself in one of the moon's great craters with the jagged rampart circling around the horizon.

The works of man seen from a distance look small in this great setting, but some of them are startling when seen from close by. On a steep mountain slope perches a massive concrete structure that has the soaring aloofness of a Tibetan monastery. This is a test stand, where the biggest rocket motors are put through their flaming paces. It really looks like an adjunct for a flight to the moon.

Far out on the desert stands an even weirder structure —a peaked concrete igloo with walls and roof as solid as the stone of a pyramid. This blockhouse has narrow slits for windows with glass many inches thick. Its strength is a prudent precaution against the possibility that a rebellious rocket may turn on its creators and rend them to smoking shreds.

Near this modern donjon keep gather strange auxiliaries: tomblike underground storage places for violent chemical fuels; lacy steelwork towers; a forest of poles and a spider web of wires. The desert for miles around is dotted with grotesque instruments. Radars sweep the sky with their pulsed electronic beams. The wide glassy eyes of cameras and theodolites stare at the launching site. Far off on the mountain rim, great telescopes with forty-inch mirrors wait to follow the rockets on their flights into space.

There are ghosts in this desert too. The hollows between the mesquite hummocks close to the launching site are sprinkled with fragments of brilliantly painted pottery. Long ago, when the Tularosa Basin was a fertile valley, it supported a dense population of Indians, whose burial grounds and building foundations can still be traced among the thorny scrub.

No one knows what happened to these ancient people. Perhaps the climate grew drier; perhaps some river changed its course or sank into the sand. At any rate they are gone. They lacked the knowledge and resourcefulness to deal with such changes of environment. They left their dead and their pottery shards and the flint fragments of their poor, weak weapons. Amateur archaeologists from the Proving Ground sometimes dig in the sand close by the launching site and find their crouched skeletons, each with a painted pot inverted over its skull.

Perhaps these departed people watch, from under the pots that cover their heads, as the rockets roar into the sky. But their ghosts do not bother the rocket men, who live in the hard, taut world of the confident present. They are too busy with their intricate jobs to worry about the failure of their predecessors on the desert.

On the day of a major shoot the whole great apparatus spreading over the desert for hundreds of miles springs into tense activity. From the metal throats of invisible loud-speakers comes a slow throbbing sound. This is a half-second beat that binds all activities to the grid of time. Jeeps and trucks scurry across the desert, raising feathers of dust. The non-human eyes of the radars swing toward the launching site, where men swarm over the steel framework that surrounds the beautiful shape of the readied rocket.

Some of the rocket's attendants are muffled from head to foot, like Arabian women, in enveloping plastic garments to protect their skins from corrosive chemicals. Others wear earphones or carry walkie-talkie radios. They pump the rocket full of fuel, quiz its electronic brains, probe its valves and pumps with sensitive instruments. They are like midget masseurs grooming a tall and graceful ballerina for her first and last appearance on the stage of a great auditorium.

Inside the massive blockhouse, which feels part like a mine, part like a radio station, part like the bridge of a battleship going into action, is a hum of tense activity and purposeful running around. Each man has a special duty, usually connected in some electronic way with the web of instruments spread over the desert. Squawking voices speak tersely with metallic tongues; vivid green lines zigzag across the faces of oscilloscopes.

On a long control panel under a slit window glows a line of little red lights. When one of them goes out, it means that some circuit is completed, some instrument far away has declared itself alert and ready. The half-second beat throbs on like a steady pulse.

Then a solemn, echoing voice comes over the loud-speaker. It says, "Zero minus thirty minutes."

This means that thirty minutes remain before the hour, the minute and the second when the rocket will fly. The men in the blockhouse, climbing over the rocket or watching across the desert become a little more tense. Their blood runs a little faster. The moment is coming.

The little red lights on the control panel wink out one by one. Voices report trouble, then trouble overcome. "Zero minus twenty minutes," chants the loud-speaker.

Trucks and jeeps loaded with men dart away from the danger area. Gates are being closed; chains are being drawn taut across distant highways. The men on the framework around the rocket are administering to it a kind of extreme unction. They check its intricate instruments for the last time and close the flush-fitting doors that cover access ports. They climb down reluctantly, and the steel framework is wheeled away, revealing the graceful shape of the doomed rocket. At this moment of unveiling, it looks like the most beautiful thing that has ever been built by man.

"Zero minus ten minutes," chants the loud-speaker.

Now a solemn hush spreads across the desert. No men are in sight. They have all fled away or gone inside the blockhouse like ants going underground ahead of an approaching shower. Only a few red lights still show on the control panel. Scientists who have worked for years on the rocket's burden of instruments are muttering over and over their profane technological prayers. Some of them finger incongruous rabbits' feet; some keep their fingers crossed like children in primary school.

"Zero minus one minute," chants the loud-speaker.

Now the impersonal voice at the unseen microphone shares the growing excitement. "Zero minus forty-five seconds," it chants in a higher key. Then: "Zero minus thirty seconds."

The last of the little red lights is gone from the control panel, leaving nothing between the rocket and its moment of glory. It stands naked and alone like a human sacrifice watched by a thousand priests. A plume of brilliant red smoke spurts from the ground beside it and drifts across the desert. This is a final visual warning to men, instruments and airplanes with no electronic ears.

"Zero minus five seconds," chants the loud-speaker. Now its words come faster. "Four—three—two—one—ZERO!"

In the tense, hushed blockhouse, the firing officer throws a switch. A stab of yellow flame and a dense white cloud of smoke burst from the tail of the rocket, and a screaming roar rolls across the desert. The rocket rises slowly at first as if an invisible hoist were drawing it upward. It wobbles a little, standing on its tail of flame. Then it gains confidence, gathers speed and shoots up toward space like a bellowing arrow. In a few seconds it is gone, leaving only a trail of smoke like a chalk mark against the blue sky.

For human eyes the flight is over, but instrument

eyes are watching. The dish antennae of distant radars turn upward after the rocket. Cameras and theodolites crane upward their jointed necks. Down from the rocket, over a sheaf of radio channels, comes a flood of information for instruments below to gather and cherish.

The nose of the rocket is packed with delicate, specialized senses. They feel the air as it rushes past, measuring its temperature, its density, its motion. Spectrographs analyze the sunlight, which grows brighter as altitude increases. Geiger tubes count the cosmic-ray particles striking fiercely out of space, and photon counters feel for X-rays flooding out of the sun.

Some of their findings are recorded on photographic films that wind into steel cylinders that are strong enough to survive the final crash of the rocket. Other findings are radioed to earth, where instrument stenographers take them down on paper as swiftly waving lines.

Sometimes the information comes in the form of audible notes that sound for all the world like a small child playing a piano. The pitch of each note varies with the instruments' readings and can be analyzed by appropriate devices. This eerie music, which is to be inscribed on magnetic tape, tells the whole tale of the rocket's effort, of its triumph above the atmosphere, and of its ultimate death.

While the rocket is waiting on its launching platform, the singing instruments in its nose play a gentle, monotonous tune. Some of the tones are continuous, like the drones of a bagpipe. Others are "sampled" periodically so that they sound like piano notes. As the rocket rises, some of the tones remain steady; others vary in pitch in a strange modernistic way. The tinkling tune continues, but it becomes irregular, as if the child who is touching the keys were growing tired or frightened. As the rocket roars up toward space, it sends down groaning, quavering sounds. These record vibration, its struggle with the atmosphere. Long, low wails mean that the rocket is yawing or rolling. The tinkling music of the sampled tones plays on bravely above this background of discord, but the child at the piano sounds desperate now. The rocket is close to the peak of its speed and struggling fiercely against the buffeting air.

As the rocket soars out of the atmosphere, the discords gradually die away. It is moving through space now, serene as an asteroid cruising around the sun, and the child at the piano plays his tinkling tune with confidence and skill.

His moment of peace in space does not last for long. The rocket reaches the top of its flight and then turns downward, tumbling over and over, toward the fringe of the atmosphere. When the air strikes it, the rocket straightens out, nose down, and points toward the spot on the desert where it will die. Vibration and yaw build up again, and discordant sounds obscure the tinkling tune. Louder and louder they grow as the rocket darts toward earth.

Radars and telescopes miles below slant downward gradually as the rocket falls. They are judging coldly just where its death will occur. The child at the piano continues his tinkling tune, now almost blotted out by warning screams from the instruments. The hard, unyielding earth rushes upward at three thousand miles per hour.

Then, without warning, the music stops. The rocket has come to its death on the desert, digging a great hole. The child at the piano will never play another tune. Nothing is left but crumpled metal and a few photographic films inscribed with precious information.

3

TESTS AND TROUBLES

Space enthusiasts who speak lightly about flights to the moon or Mars should be privileged to watch a White Sands rocket shoot. It would give them a sobering glimpse of difficulties ahead. The rockets that roar into the sky above the New Mexico desert are primitive things when compared with what real space vehicles must be. They rise only a few hundred miles at most, and their speed is hardly one-tenth of the speed that would be needed to blast them free of the earth. They carry no human crews, and they all crash to utter ruin.

But these crude "beasts" (some rocket men call them "beasts"; others call them "birds") are the best that space-striving man has to offer at present. To White

Sands come the highest products of technological achievement: strange metals with treated surfaces to resist the white-hot scour of racing gases; electronic brains packed with transistors or tiny vacuum tubes and finished as precisely as microscope lenses; pumps no bigger than coffee cups that can push corrosive fuels as fast as the massive flow of irrigation canals.

Marching into White Sands comes a continuous parade of new and incredible instruments—those thousands of specialized senses with which man must augment the senses built into his body. They take their stations in the central laboratories, in the blockhouse or in solid little huts dotted over the desert. There they get busily to work, flashing their impressions on fast-flowing strips of photographic film or scribbling with delicate pens on streams of paper like quick-fingered stenographers writing a strange shorthand.

The men who govern the instruments are as skilled as they. To White Sands come top experts on electronics, optics, solid-state physics, chemistry, metallurgy, mathematics and astronomy. Some of them stay for years; others stay only long enough to make specific contributions to this remote deposit of technical virtuosity.

What these experts do is mostly secret. White Sands, officially, is an Army Ordnance center for the development and testing of new weapons—intelligent and terrible weapons. Some of them are mechanical falcons that scream into the air at a human command and run down and destroy anything flying there. Others are avenging angels designed to fly over continents, steering by the stars, and strike down offending cities in the flash of a nuclear explosion.

The men of White Sands do not talk lightly about these fearful projects. They know that they are necessary and will always be necessary as long as mankind is committed to a course of mutual destruction. But when the quiet of night has crept over the desert and the brilliant, many-colored stars flash in the clear sky, the men of White Sands like to turn their thoughts, half-apologetically, toward a more peaceful project—the conquest and occupation of the vacuum above their heads.

Even the enlisted men—some of them learned G.I.s who play hot chess in the crowded barracks and chat in the chow lines about quantum mechanics—realize that they are working at the closest place on earth to space. They appreciate both the accomplishments of man on his march towards space and the enormous difficulties that still lie in his path. They know, for instance, that rockets are as temperamental as the graceful, smooth-flanked dancers that they so strangely resemble.

In the early days when Americans were first learning to fly captured German V-2 rockets, one of these flaming monsters rose from the launching site with a mutinous plot in its gyroscopic brain. Instead of rising vertically, as a good rocket should, it veered toward the south. Its launchers—both Americans and Germans—stared after it helplessly. There was nothing that they could do.

Across the Rio Grande fifty miles away, the city of Juarez, Mexico, was having a fiesta. Its wide, garish main street at the end of the bridge from El Paso was packed with a gay crowd. Bands were playing and fireworks cracked overhead. Slanting down from the north at three thousand miles per hour came the rebellious V-2. It shot across the crowd and buried itself with a vast concussion in a hillside cemetery just outside the city.

The Mexicans rather enjoyed this super-firework; they are friends of death when it comes in heroic form. But the authorities at White Sands are still acutely conscious of what that V-2 might have done if its rebellious brain had chosen a slightly different course.

One result of this international incident, which almost produced a catastrophe, was an elaborate safety system. Another was the construction of the massive blockhouse. Not long after it was completed, a second V-2 rebelled, made a great loop in the air and screamed within six hundred feet of the blockhouse, trailing its tail of flame.

The captured V-2s were tamed at last, but all rockets, especially the new ones, contain within them the seeds of possible disaster. To make sure that they will perform as expected, they are sometimes given static tests while held securely to the ground. Even this sort of test, intended to forestall disaster, may go wrong in spectacular ways.

Not long ago, one of the biggest rockets was being tested statically. It stood on its tail, screaming, while floods of flame and smoke shot out of its shackled motor. Then it began to struggle fiercely like a captive wild animal suddenly conscious of its bonds. The hold-downs broke. The rocket soared upward and hid behind the blue sky.

A panicky pulse of alarm swept across White Sands. The many-eyed net of instruments had not been watching, but the radars sprang to attention in seconds and swept the echoing sky. Telescopes groped for the fugitive rocket. Radio beams raced after it like lariats flung into space. No one knew where it had gone, and it had enough range at worst to fall as far north as Santa Fe or as far south as Chihuahua in Mexico.

The men of White Sands will give few details about the rocket that got away. They will not tell—or perhaps they do not know—whether their electronic lariats caught it and controlled it before it climbed out of the atmosphere. At any rate it fell in an uninhabited spot and did not dig its great crater in the plaza of Santa Fe.

There have been lesser disasters too, a multitude of them, and there will be more. White Sands is an outpost on the lawless frontier of technology. Each new rocket is acrawl with vindictive "bugs" that conspire to destroy it, and its creators too. To eliminate these bugs, every rocket part, even the tiniest of them, must be tested over and over.

The first of the testing is done in factories where the parts are made. They are strained and twisted, heated and cooled—even such inconsequential trifles as bolts and sealing rings. Then they are assembled into larger units and tested more elaborately. The rockets' electronic brains are put through intelligence tests. The

aerodynamic performance of their fins and control surfaces is studied minutely in wind tunnels.

Most spectacular are the tests of the motors, which
are done in desolate well-fenced places far from protesting neighbors. Even well away from the test stands, these
sites have an oppressive feeling of tense, pessimistic caution. Danger signs scream their warnings in loud colors.
Visitors are searched for matches and cigarette lighters.
Walls of buildings are apt to be many feet thick. If
liquid oxygen is one of the chemicals used in the motors,
it bubbles coldly and silently in gigantic thermos bot-
tles buried in concrete. Pipes carry upward the oxygen
vapor, which drifts away from their tips in thin violet
plumes.

The rocket motors themselves are surprisingly small.
One type, which has power enough to drive several
ocean liners, is a graceless pinch-waisted thing made of
sheet metal and about as big as two bushel baskets.
Massive steelwork holds it to a frame, and a tangle of
pipes and tubes leads into its bulbous head.

The men who run the test sit at a control panel behind many feet of concrete, and ranks of instruments
stand at attention to record the motor's performance.
Spectators, if any have been admitted, are kept at a good
distance and advised to stuff their ears with wads of
cotton.

Crouching close to the motor's tailpipe are television
cameras which serve as expendable spectators, flashing
their impressions to screens in the control room. If
something goes wrong with the test, these non-human

observers may die. Often they do. At one of the test sites, the crumpled remains of the camera casualties are buried in a special graveyard where little white crosses commemorate their uncomplaining self-sacrifice.

To watch the test of a rocket motor is a shattering experience. Without the slightest warning, an enormous flame juts out of the tailpipe. The eyes cringe from its light, and a wave of heat beats against the skin. An indescribable bellowing sound pokes like an ice pick into cotton-stuffed ears. Even worse than the bellowing is a high-pitched waspish scream. This is the faintly audible edge of the motor's ultrasonic sound. It tears at the heart and groin and raises knife-edged vibrations echoing inside the skull.

But the screaming, bellowing flame is a beautiful thing. When certain fuels are used, it is so bright that it sears the eyes through filters that shut out the sunlight. With other fuels the flame is a delicate, transparent violet with a line of diamond-shaped plates that look like gold leaf trembling in its center. These burnished leaves are caused by shock waves zigzagging through the flame. When the fuel is shut off, they chase one another into the motor like rabbits running down a hole.

The flame of one experimental fuel, a boron hydride, is brilliant green, and it fades into billows of purplish smoke. No Chinese dragon flying through the air was ever arrayed in colors as gay as these.

In some test setups the flame points horizontally; its gases scour the ground, leaving hot, charred rocks where their tongue has licked. Sometimes the flame is directed downward against a steel plate cooled from above and below by floods of cold water. If the plate were made of concrete, as in some earlier tests, it would be destroyed by the flame, many inches of its substance clawed into gravel and dust.

The men who know about guided missiles will not say how many tests have been successful, certifying a rocket motor for future use in the sky. This is one of those dull statistics that has great military value. But they admit that in most cases the tests are still necessary, even at the risk of damaging a motor. The art of making rocket motors has not reached a point where all the pinch-waisted monsters can be expected to perform without experience.

Another kind of testing is done in quiet rooms. One of these simulated proving grounds is on Manhattan Island in a building which looks, except for the watchful guards outside its door, like a small factory making toys or dresses. Another is in the dry hills behind Pasadena, California. There are no screaming motors in these sheltered places and no other parts of a rocket. Instead, ranged around the walls, are panels of gleaming black plastic with row upon row of switches and dials and little winking red lights. These are the stolid impersonal faces of electronic computers whose brains of metal and glass can solve, in fractions of a second, problems that would employ for a lifetime a task force of mathematicians.

Only skilled mathematicians can get much of a thrill out of these flights by computer, but men with sufficient knowledge watch their outcome as tensely as if they were at White Sands. In preparation for the flight they have given the computer all the necessary data about the imaginary rocket that its brain contains. Dials are set to represent external factors such as gravitation and air resistance. When the machine is fully briefed, it knows what to expect from every part of the imaginary rocket—except a single crucial part that has not yet been tested.

The mathematicians know that this new part—perhaps a control surface—can have only a certain range of effects on the rocket's flight. They give the computer a formula that represents one extreme of this range. Then they set the machine to thinking. A blizzard of electronic impulses crisscrosses through its brain, and out come figures that tell how the simulated rocket has performed in flight.

Sometimes the flight is a failure. Sometimes it is a disaster. The simulated rocket that exists only in the computer's electronic mind may shake itself to pieces or turn back in the air to crash upon the imaginary desert.

Then comes another flight with the part to be tested set in a slightly different way. The success of this test, too, is written down in the books. At last after many imaginary flights, the behavior of the new component is as well understood as if twenty or thirty great rockets, each costing a quarter of a million dollars, had been flown into space at White Sands to crash on the real desert.

As the men of White Sands stare up into space at

night when the bright stars are glittering, they are proud of the achievements of rocket-building man. But they also remember the tests—the big tests and the little tests —and how many of them have failed. So when they are asked how near man has come to accomplishing space flight, they reply that the road is long and rough and that the part ahead is even more difficult than the part behind.

One philosophical rocketeer pointed to the fact that man's body stands midway in size between the atoms that it contains and the great galaxies that float beyond the stars. Man's position, he said, on the road toward space flight is somewhat similar: he has come a long way, but the road ahead is long. A deep technological faith, which can be as strong as religious faith, is needed—and is not lacking.

Each hotel room in El Paso, the gateway to White Sands, has its Gideon Bible, and one of the rocket men (who is somewhat abashed by his quasi-religious deviation), tells how he opened his Gideon during an empty evening. He had never read the Old Testament with attention before, but now that he had worked at White Sands the ancient people of Genesis and Exodus came suddenly to life. They were operating in an arid country very like New Mexico, with the hot sun beating down on their heads or the brilliant stars leading their thoughts upward.

He closed that Gideon Bible in his hotel room and a long, vivid parade marched through his mind. Now he could see the strategy and goal of technological history.

The industrial revolution, he realized, began in Western Europe where the skies are low and dull and the stars are dim. Here men first took control of power and flame and speed. Under those dull skies they used their new techniques for practical purposes: gathering wealth and waging wars. But now the industrial men of Western Europe have penetrated into a desert—the American Southwest—which has the spiritual inspiration of Palestine or Arabia. Their thoughts have grown long and high like the thoughts of grave Bedouins sitting under the stars. The people of the Old Testament, the rocket man thought to himself, would see nothing ridiculous in a project to fly into space. They would write psalms about it and honor those men who made progress toward such an ideal.

4

DAEDALUS AND NEWTON

Sometimes during intervals in the rush of their work, the rocket men climb backward along the framework of time and retrace the steps that they have taken to reach their present station. The yearning to fly into the sky is almost as old as man. In the years when the ancient Greeks were as confident and aspiring as modern Americans are, a space pioneer, Daedalus, used the best technology of mythological times (feathers attached with wax) to make an assault on space.

Daedalus was too old to be a space cadet, so his young son Icarus took over that function. Like many a reckless young man of today, he went beyond the safety factors of his equipment. He flew too near the sun. Its heat melted the wax. His feathers came off, and Icarus crashed like a rocket at White Sands.

Those were the early hopeful days. Then Greek astronomers learned that the sun and moon are not small bodies passing over the earth a few miles above its surface. They realized little by little that they are far away and that the atmosphere does not reach them. So something better than wings would have to be developed before man could fly even to the nearby moon.

Shortly after this realization, Greece was conquered by unimaginative Rome, and Rome plunged into the cringing darkness of the Middle Ages. For more than a thousand years Western man did not challenge the sky, but at some time during this period the less benighted Chinese invented the vehicle that can cruise into space.

Rockets are simple things. Probably the first rocket was intended to be a firecracker to enliven the Chinese New Year. If a firecracker is made imperfectly, it may blow out at one end and snap a few feet through the air. When it is made a little stronger and its powder is ignited at an unclosed end, it flies considerably farther. To control its direction of flight, the Chinese added a slender stick that had the same effect as the carefully engineered fins on the tails of modern rockets. Now they flew straight and added pleasant excitement to Chinese celebrations. They were also used slightly in war; in Arab countries rockets are still called "Chinese arrows."

In due course rockets came to Europe, and philosophical Europeans wondered about the forces that shoot them into the air. Probably no one at this time connected these playthings with flight into space. Europeans realized clearly by this time that even the moon, the earth's nearest neighbor, lies enormously far away. They told entertaining tales about flights to the moon, but none of them was intended to be taken seriously.

The next and greatest step toward space flight was made in a quiet English garden by the ill-tempered Isaac Newton. With a burst of genius which was not equaled in intellectual history until the time of Einstein, he discovered the laws that govern the behavior of moving bodies.

Newton's laws are not difficult. They merely state that:

1. A body at rest remains at rest, and a body in motion continues to move at constant speed along a straight line, unless the body is acted upon in either case by an unbalanced force.
2. An unbalanced force acting upon a body causes it to accelerate in the direction of the force, and the acceleration is directly proportional to the unbalanced force and inversely proportional to the mass of the body.
3. For every action, there is an equal and opposite reaction.
4. Each particle of matter attracts every other particle with a force that is directly proportional to the product of their masses and inversely proportional to the square of the distance between them.

One of the effects of these rules was to enable scientists to predict accurately the motions of the planets. This technique of "celestial mechanics" provides all that is needed for plotting the courses of space ships. A man-made body moving among the planets obeys precisely the same laws that the planets do.

Newton's laws also explain why rockets fly. Their motion forward is the reaction to the motion of their gases backward. It was not long after Newton that men realized that rockets, unlike birds or kites or other flying objects of the time, need no air to fly in. Their propulsive force is even more effective in the vacuum of space than it is in the atmosphere.

The world of Sir Isaac Newton was, of course, a long way from space flight. Man's best vehicles were still pulled by horses or sails. But Newton's laws were beautiful instruments that enabled the minds of man to travel upward into space, guided by rules much more exact than imagination.

On Newton's laws was built, little by little, the fascinating play-science of astronautics. Men of the nineteenth century could not leave the earth. They could not even leave the ground except in clumsy balloons, but they could imagine flights into space and plot their trajectories accurately by means of Newton's laws.

The most famous of these fictional but reasonably scientific journeys was described in *From the Earth to the Moon* by Jules Verne. Verne made the great mistake of not using a rocket. He flew in a cannon shell. The cannon was buried in the earth and fired upward vertically when the moon was in the right position.

For reasons which were probably well understood at the time, this maneuver would not have worked. For one thing, no cannon shell could attain sufficient initial speed, and even if it could, its skin would have been washed away by friction with the air. Another failing of shells as space vehicles is that they start too suddenly. Jules Verne was conscious of this, and the crew of his space shell took elaborate precautions to keep themselves from being crushed by acceleration forces. They would have been crushed nevertheless; the forces in a cannon shell at the moment of explosion are much too great for human bodies to stand.

But once the shell was well out into space it traveled on the clean, sure rails of Newton's wonderful laws. Granted sufficient speed for their shell, the astronomers who advised Jules Verne could have plotted a trip to Venus or Mars with excellent accuracy.

Jules Verne wrote in 1865, and there were men around at that time who could have advised him to use a rocket. It would be interesting to know why he did not do so. Perhaps his reasons were literary. Cannon were then the lords of battle and had long been a specialty of his French countrymen. Rockets, on the other hand, were inconsequential amusements. They had had a brief military vogue several generations before, and the phrase "by the rocket's red glare" in the American national anthem is a relic of this time. But their inaccuracy had brought them to low repute, and Jules Verne may have felt that the discredited rocket would not be a convincing vehicle for a literary trip to the moon.

Rockets have gathered about them a formidable tangle of physics, but the principle that makes them fly is so simple that it can be understood without the slightest difficulty. A child's toy balloon, tightly inflated and allowed to flutter from the fingers, works on the rocket principle. It has a chamber filled with compressed air, and this is analogous to the rocket's combustion chamber, which is filled with hot gases under high compression. When the balloon's neck is closed, the air presses equally against all sides of the chamber. The forces that it exerts can be visualized as small arrows pointing outward. The arrows of force counteract one another, so the balloon does not move.

When the neck of the balloon is opened, the air rushes out through it. The arrow of force at that point has nothing solid to push against, and the arrow of force at the other end is no longer balanced. It pushes against its side of the balloon, moving it in that direction. The balloon whirls across the room until its stock of compressed air has been exhausted. In exactly the same way, the hot compressed gases formed by the burning fuel in a rocket's combustion chamber rush freely out of one end of it and press against the other end, forcing the rocket forward.

The air surrounding the rocket motor performs no necessary function. Indeed it is a disadvantage; it tends to hinder the escape of the gases and thus reduces the unbalanced force that pushes against the forward end of the chamber. This is why rockets need no air for their action, and why they work most efficiently in space, where their gases roar into a vacuum.

Rocket men do not think habitually of the unbalanced push at the motor's forward end. It is more convenient to deal with the escaping gases, whose mass and speed taken together are a measure of the forward push. The careful, exact design of the motor's throat is to let the gases escape as easily as possible.

Since the speed of the escaping gases is proportional to the pressure in the chamber, all rockets—even the primitive ones that impressed holiday crowds for a thousand years—have some sort of strong-walled chamber to hold the pressure of the gases and a neck narrow enough to allow pressure to accumulate. If the open neck is too large, the pressure in the chamber remains small and the unbalanced force at its forward end is also small. If the neck is narrow, the pressure becomes high and the rocket is more efficient, but thick, strong walls are needed to keep the chamber from bursting. Their weight, which must be carried on the rocket's flight, is an unproductive burden.

The great weight of the thick-walled combustion chamber is the principal reason why rockets that burn solid gunpowder do not perform impressively. All the powder must be packed inside the thick wall. When more powder is carried, the weight of the chamber grows proportionately, so there is little advantage in giving the rocket more fuel. Airplanes would have a similar disadvantage if the fuel tanks built into their wings had to have thick steel walls.

In the late nineteenth century, when rockets were still hardly more than spectacular entertainments, scientists could figure how fast they would fly, and therefore how high they would rise, if their fuel were burned efficiently and their structure were light. Even with gunpowder, which contains comparatively little energy, the theoretical possibilities were astonishingly good. Even gunpowder rockets should fly well out of the atmosphere.

None of them did fly so high because their solid propellent had to be packed inside a large, thick-walled combustion chamber, and this made them too heavy. The obvious way to get around this difficulty was to build a rocket using liquid fuel. It could be carried in light, thin-walled tanks and pumped as needed into a small combustion chamber.

When the early theoretical rocket men figured what could be done with this device, they reared back from their calculations in a state of bug-eyed excitement. A liquid-fuel rocket could soar right off the earth and cruise among the planets. Hundreds of eager scribblers began to cover paper with figures, and the play-science of astronautics began to think of itself as a practical technology. Historians of rocketry can point to nineteenth-century physicists who foresaw most of the rocket techniques that are being worked out today.

However attractive the principle, no liquid-fueled rocket flew until 1926 when a strange, bitter, suspicious man, Professor Robert H. Goddard, fired the first one into the air near Worcester, Massachusetts. Goddard's rocket, fueled with alcohol and liquid oxygen, was a feeble thing only a few feet long. It rose only a mile or so but its success in flying at all started a wave of rocket excitement. It also got Goddard run out of Massachusetts as a menace to life and serenity. Even more bitter and secretive, he continued his experiments in New Mexico, that state whose empty stretches, so much like the surface of the moon, seem to attract the rocket men.

The success of Goddard's experiments swept around the world. Men in many countries began to think about space flight not as an impractical dream, but as a dream which had at last some chance of practicality. By the 1930s, interplanetary societies had been organized in Britain, the United States and Germany. Their members were regarded as lunatics, but they rather enjoyed the title; the word "lunatic" means by derivation an inhabitant of the moon.

One of the sad things about really great inventions is that they start their lives as delicate larvae with no great viability. A small invention, a mere detail such as a cheap process of making a commercial chemical out of natural gas, attracts an entourage of enterprisers who smell fast money. Larger, more radical inventions do not promise profit in their early years. Both the airplane and the rocket needed the forced, unnatural feeding of a world war to bring them to adolescence.

Fortunately for those inventions, if for nothing else, the wars came along on schedule. The Wright brothers' fluttering airplane, hardly more than a powered box kite, grew in a semi-generation into a deadly predator over no man's land. In almost exactly the same span of time, Goddard's little rockets grew into the great German V-2s which almost, but not quite, dominated World War II.

5

SECRET WORLD OF GUIDED MISSILES

So new are practical rockets that the man who is responsible for a large part of their development lives today on a pleasant hillside street in Huntsville, Alabama. He is only forty-one years old. He has a beautiful young wife and two beautiful children, and he looks out of the picture window of his new house and regrets that Alabama's summers do not encourage the year-round greenness of his native Germany.

This handsome blond man is named Wernher von Braun. Now he works on guided missiles in the vast arsenal of U.S. Army Ordnance that dominates Huntsville. When he was eighteen years old and a student in

Berlin, he read about Goddard's rockets and saw their possibilities. He looked upward at the moon sailing coldly over Germany and resolved that he would go there. He still wants to go to the moon, and although he lives and works in a foreign and formerly hostile country, the extraordinary force of his personality is felt throughout the growing world of modern rocketry. Whenever men meet to talk about rockets, and more of them meet every day, the name von Braun touches off a blizzard of controversy.

Von Braun was wartime chief of the Peenemünde center which developed the great rocket that Nazi propagandists named *Vergeltungswaffe Zwei* (Revenge-weapon Two). By his own account, he made use of German military funds to further his project of space flight and was not primarily interested in building weapons for the Nazis. However this may be, he accomplished both objectives. His V-2s started a military revolution. They also laid the foundations of the vigorous guided-missile business, out of which true space flight has a chance to grow.

The wartime V-2 was not strictly a guided missile. It was a rocket forty-six feet long that weighed fourteen tons when fueled with alcohol and liquid oxygen. Its simple-minded brain could sense nothing more than direction and speed. As it rose vertically, a gang of little gyroscopes steered it in the right direction. When it reached the proper speed, another gadget cut off the fuel, thus limiting its range. From then on it flew a "ballistic course" like an artillery shell; neither its launchers nor the enemy could control it in any way.

The V-2s were neither accurate nor dependable, but they were an enormous advance over prewar rockets, which were merely dangerous toys. If the Germans had had time to improve some of their mechanical details and give them a better guidance system, the V-2s might have knocked London to rubble and disrupted Allied preparations for the invasion of Normandy. Luckily, the V-2s were forced into production while still imperfect; they wandered all over the map, many of them falling in France or the English Channel. Most of those that did reach England dug harmless holes in open fields or vacant lots.

A people less resolute than the British might have been panicked by the V-2s, against which they had no defense at all. The great rockets stabbed down from the sky at more than 3,000 miles per hour. Their speed made them invisible. It made them silent, too; they moved many times faster than the sound of their coming.

When a V-2 hit the ground, it blasted a huge crater, the explosive force of its one-ton warhead contributing less to the destruction than did the sheer kinetic energy of its speeding mass. Then, as the rubble settled, a long rumbling roar poured down out of the sky. This was he rocket's shock wave, which had been left far behind.

If full-scale war comes to the world again, this pattern will be repeated with spectacular improvements. Crude though they were, the V-2s came within a hair's readth of devastating success. Their range of 150 miles was plenty for many military purposes. Their accuracy could have been improved with a little time and effort. If their warheads had been atomic bombs, they would have destroyed whole cities instead of digging holes in the ground.

After World War II was over, the United States and Soviet Russia saw nothing more clearly than the promise of military rockets. Both nations set to work frantically at the point where the Germans had stopped. Both realized that rocket-propelled missiles are potentially the lords of war, capable of relegating airplanes to the status of transport vehicles.

Russian accomplishments in the field of missiles are, of course, unknown. Spies and fugitives have probably brought a good deal of information about the Russian program, but such reports, reliable or not, have been kept secret. To publish them would tell the Russians how much we know, and it might enable them to plug the leaks through which the information came.

A common belief in guided-missile circles is that the Russians have built a large number of slightly improved V-2s, but have not made much progress with the more advanced missiles. A more disquieting rumor is that they may have perfected an intercontinental missile that the Germans were developing at the end of the war. Designed for a range of about three thousand miles, it was intended to hit New York from bases in German-held Europe.

The American missile program, too, has been kept remarkably quiet. Airplane designers, who chatter glibly about new bombers or fighters, shut their mouths like snapping turtles when guided missiles are mentioned. With a few exceptions, even the names of the missiles are unknown to the public. The test ranges and factories are closely guarded, and almost nothing has been told about the design, performance or production of the new weapons. It is known, however, that several billion dollars have already been spent on guided missiles and that many more billions have been earmarked for them.

Not all of these great sums, perhaps not much of them, will go into rockets on the model of the V-2s. Since the end of the war, missiles have evolved with startling rapidity, like the primitive ratlike mammals that diverged at the end of the age of reptiles into animals as different as whales and bats. Their development has drawn into it all branches of technology and also many apparently unrelated sciences such as mathematical logic and neurophysiology. The proper placement of the missiles on enemy targets employs economists and students of history and mass psychology.

The direct descendants of the V-2 are now called ground-to-ground missiles. They are of many types, built for different purposes. Some are long-range artillery to place conventional or atomic explosives close behind enemy lines. More ambitious types are intended to fly much farther, perhaps halfway around the earth. Rocket men agree that there is no theoretical limit to a missile's range. The cost of tossing them from Maine to Moscow (or from Poland to Washington) will always be great, but nuclear explosives make the effort a sound military investment.

Some missiles designed to be launched from the ground follow the general plan of the V-2. It had a single rocket motor that was only strong enough to start it climbing upward rather slowly. While it was gathering speed, it was steered by graphite vanes set in the stream of hot gas from the motor's tailpipe. Taking their signals from the rocket's gyroscopic brain, the vanes tilted slightly, deflecting the gases in the right direction to keep the rocket from wobbling. The vanes burned out quickly, but not until the rocket had attained great speed. Then the rudders on its tail fins took over and steered it like an airplane. The same initial stability can be assured by turning the motor and its gas stream slightly from side to side.

A more popular system at present is to use a launching "booster." The rocket proper is fitted into the forward end of a cylindrical body with a rocket motor of its own, which gives a large thrust for a very short time. Most boosters use a solid propellent (some kind of gunpowder) that burns for as little as one second. This violent push tosses the rocket upward so quickly that it gains steering speed before it has time to wobble. When the booster burns out, it falls back to earth with a screaming, whimpering sound, and the missile continues climbing under its own power.

Some long-range ground-to-ground missiles will keep within the atmosphere. This has several advantages. Even a little air makes conventional steering possible, and if the rocket is flying fast enough, small wings will support it and keep it on a course to match the curve of the earth. Another advantage is the possible saving of fuel. More than half the fuel carried by a rocket is oxygen or some chemical compound that contains oxygen. A missile that stays within the atmosphere can gather its own oxygen, combining it with fuel in a ram jet, a kind of engine that resembles a rocket motor except that it gets its oxygen from air "rammed" into it by the missile's speed. The saving in weight of oxygen may more than make up for the resistance of the air that the missile must pass through.

The great disadvantage of staying within the atmosphere is the intense heat caused by air friction. This is a serious business; many a missile designer has seen an impossible temperature stare him in the face out of his calculations. Even in the high, thin fringe of the atmosphere, missiles moving at much desired speeds will get so hot that their skins, if made of conventional materials, will turn into metal raindrops.

Heat-resisting alloys that are used in the turbine blades of jet engines are not a satisfactory answer. They are expensive, hard to fabricate and demand scarce materials. Besides, if the missile's skin is allowed to get too hot, it will communicate too much heat to the missile's interior. This cannot be permitted; at very moderate temperatures the missile's brain will cease to function (like a man's brain that has been boiled), and its fuels will evaporate or perhaps explode.

There is no chance of cooling the missile by allowing

the outside air to blow freely through its interior. For one thing, the air at very high altitudes is not always cold; at some levels, sunlight makes it hot enough to melt many metals. Even where the air is cold, it would have little cooling effect. As soon as it is permitted to enter the missile, it is slowed down by friction and compressed strongly. This makes it so hot that it heats the missile's interior instead of cooling it.

Mechanical cooling devices on the general plan of household refrigerators are completely inadequate. They take too much power, and they have nowhere to dump the heat extracted from the missile.

The problem of heat has not been licked as yet, though several promising leads are being followed vigorously. One device uses "ice cubes" of solid air whose gradual evaporation cools the missile's insides. This works only for short periods. Another trick is to cover the missile's skin with steel "shingles" that can resist great heat. They are spot-welded to the main skin of the missile in such a way that they touch it in only a few places. The outside surface of each shingle is coated with a black porcelainlike material that radiates heat rapidly. The inside has a coating that radiates as slowly as possible. When the shingles get red hot or white hot, they are free to expand without buckling. Most of their heat radiates outward; comparatively little of it crosses the open space and penetrates the missile's skin.

Other long-range, ground-to-ground missiles fly right out of the atmosphere as the V-2s did. When they leave the last of the air behind, they are impossible to steer, so they must be set accurately on their courses during the rising leg of their flight. When they plunge down toward their targets, they are traveling at many thousands of miles per hour. Then their aim can be corrected only slightly, perhaps not at all.

One promising modification is to provide these ballistic rockets with small but sufficient wings. As soon as they reach the atmosphere on their descending curve, their wings grip the air. The control surfaces in their tail fins steer them in a long flat glide. This increases their range and gives their guidance system a chance to steer them to their targets.

Rockets designed for even greater range may proceed in a series of jumps like stones skipped from water. Each time they come down to the atmosphere, their wings and tail surfaces will steer them up again into empty space. During each stay in the atmosphere, their electronic brains will have an opportunity to correct their courses. This was the plan of that special custom job with which the Germans intended to hit New York.

A bizarre type of long-range rocket may use wings to give it "negative lift." If any missile gets flying too fast (more than 17,000 miles per hour) on a roughly horizontal course, it tends to move out into space instead of following the curvature of the earth. This can be prevented by wings that are set to hold it down instead of holding it up. When its speed drops below the critical point, the wings change their attitude slightly. Now they hold it up instead of holding it down. One missile manufacturer has predicted that missiles will fly at 18,000 m.p.h. If he means this seriously, he must have solved to his own satisfaction the troublesome problem of holding the missile down.

The missile men are not allowed to say how many of these ideas (and there are more fantastic ones) have been put into practice. Some of them have been tried and more will certainly follow. The rocket range at White Sands, which is forty miles wide and more than one hundred and twenty miles long, is now considered inadequate for testing long-range missiles. They are flown over the Atlantic from the east coast of Florida, and instrument stations to observe their performance have been dotted over the Bahama Islands.

Even this range, about five hundred miles long, is considered inadequate too. The latest instrument stations that have been mentioned officially are in Puerto Rico, one thousand miles from Florida. The British have a range in Australia that crosses fifteen hundred miles of uninhabited desert and extends into the Indian Ocean, where few ships sail. Some of the missiles that need such distances for their proper testing may not be very far from true space flight.

There is a general feeling in the long-range missile business that the problem of propulsion is much closer to solution than the problem of guidance and control. Short-range missiles can be steered by radio signals of various types, but when a missile passes beyond the horizon, radio signals that follow straight lines can no longer reach it dependably around the curve of the earth. This distance can be extended somewhat by re-laying the signals from a high-flying airplane, but the range is increased by only a few hundred miles, and the relay plane is exposed to enemy attack or inter-ference.

Proposals to lick this problem have an eerie sound. One plan is to launch a continuous stream of missiles. They will fly in Indian file several hundred miles apart and will keep in touch by radio, each missile except the first acting as a relay station above the curve of the earth. The missile in the lead can be steered by radio signals sent from missile to missile over the many-legged channel. When it has been directed down to its target, the second missile in line takes over the lead position and is sent to its target in turn. This procedure, which is rather like playing a garden hose whose drop-lets are atom bombs, continues until the stock of mis-siles has been exhausted. By that time, it is hoped, most of the enemy's vitals will be crippled.

A failing of the garden-hose system as described above is that it lacks what engineers call feedback. For proper control, the lead missile should have a way of contin-uously reporting its position in relation to its target. One way of supplying feedback is to provide each mis-sile with radar or television eyes to watch the terrain below. The picture of what the missile sees is sent back to the launching base, several thousand miles away, over the chain of flying relays. Officers sitting before a screen watch a moving map of distant enemy country. Rivers, lakes and cities pass slowly across it as the missile speeds toward its assigned target. If it veers from the proper course, a gentle radio hint sent over the relays puts it right again.

At last the selected target appears on the screen. An officer touches a control key and turns the missile downward toward the heart of a city or an industrial complex. Larger and larger the target grows as the missile plunges down. Then the picture vanishes as a vast explosion vaporizes the missile. Another picture flashes on the screen as the second missile in line reports what it is seeeing with its non-human eyes.

This daisy chain of destruction sounds like a nightmarish dream out of a work of science fiction. It is no dream. It may never be attempted because some other device looks more promising, but it is not impossible. Crewless airplanes that report what they see over television channels have been flown successfully for several years. The operator sitting in front of a screen at a distant base sees just what he would see if he were in the airplane's cockpit. He watches the ground passing below. Simultaneously, he watches the airplane's instruments and works its controls by means of radio signals.

Many such pilotless planes have been flown over American cities. From their safe and comfortable chairs in distant bases, the operators watch on a television screen the flow of the city's traffic and the drift of the smoke from its factory chimneys. If they chose, they could crash the plane against any tall building. They would see the same sights and could steer the same course through the eyes of a guided missile plunging down out of the sky.

Another school of designers believes that long-range missiles must learn to fly on their own without guidance from a base and find their targets by means of a self-contained navigation system. This requires that they follow some frame of reference that will guide them to the known position of their target on the surface of the earth. The most obvious guides are the stars, which were used for this purpose by seamen long before the invention of the compass.

To steer accurately by the stars, a missile will need an extremely intelligent electronic brain. Small telescopes peeking out of its nose will pick up a specified pair or trio of stars and keep centered upon them. This information, when combined with sidereal time (which keeps track of the earth's turning) keeps the missile informed of its position above the surface of the earth. Instructions recorded on a magnetic tape flowing through the missile's brain tell it just where it should be at each moment of time. The missile's brain checks with the stars and keeps its actual position matched to the tape's instructions. The target is represented by a theoretical point under the stars. When the missile approaches this point, the programming tape turns it downward and explodes its nuclear warhead at the most effective altitude.

Some designers believe that a missile should not rely on the stars alone; it should also check its position by sensing the earth's magnetic field, which varies in strength and direction with changes of latitude and longitude. Unfortunately, the Russians do not provide the non-Communist world with accurate magnetic maps of their territories. If they did, the problem of sending missiles to vital Soviet targets would be somewhat simpler.

An entirely different school of missile design believes that long-range missiles can be "programmed" at their bases with such extreme accuracy that they will hit any target on earth by means of a kind of postgraduate dead reckoning. Merely pointing them in the right direction and cutting off their fuel to give them the desired range is not sufficient. This is what the V-2s did, and it was the main cause of their notorious inaccuracy.

Better results are expected from a special instrument that senses and records every force, no matter how small, that affects the missile during its entire flight. It measures the large force of the motors' thrust and the continuing pull of gravitation. It must also be sensitive enough to measure the push or pull of the winds and also the changing drag of air of varying density.

If the instrument detects all these forces and allows for them properly, the missile's electronic brain can figure out where it is at every moment. Then it compares its actual position with a programming tape and makes the proper corrections to zero it on the target.

Such systems of automatic navigation may prove accurate enough to bring a missile to the general vicinity of its target. They are not likely to insure pinpoint hits. So the missile designers may turn to the weirdest device of all—an electronic intelligence that can read and follow a map just like a human navigator.

When a radar-equipped airplane flies over certain kinds of terrain, especially ocean shorelines, lakes and the estuaries of rivers, a clear, sharp outline shows on its radarscope. The pattern of the shoreline is easy to recognize; the pilot can steer by it just as if he were watching the ground below.

A map-reading missile will do the same thing without human participation. Through its brain will flow a continuous strip map, probably on microfilm, of the territory that it will fly over as seen by radar. Its own radar will observe the actual terrain that is passing below and display its outline on its scope. A special map-reading unit that can recognize patterns will adjust the missile's course until the radar image of the real terrain matches the microfilm. All the missile need then do is to keep the two images superimposed. As the microfilm flows through its brain, the missile bears down on the target, following a river or other conspicuous guide. The flowing film also tells it when to turn down sharply and explode its atom bomb.

There are other projects too—even more bizarre— which depend on physical effects that are hard to describe and are not well understood. And while the guidance experts work on these navigation systems, they are backed up by other tribes of experts whose jobs are just as strange.

Rocket fuels, for instance, are under intensive study by men who do not mind working with nature's most unpleasant chemicals. A safe rocket fuel is a contradiction in terms. Into a rocket's fuel tanks must be packed as much energy as possible, and this energy must be released by combustion as quickly as possible. The V-2s combined ethyl alcohol with liquid oxygen, but alcohol is already partially oxidized, and so it does not yield as much energy as many other fuels do. Liquid oxygen is unsatisfactory because it must be kept in elaborately insulated tanks to prevent it from boiling away.

So the fuel experts are testing many other combinations. A popular pair at present is aniline as the fuel and fuming nitric acid as the oxygen-carrier. Neither of these liquids is nice to have around. Both are poisonous, and the acid is corrosive and gives off dangerous fumes. Most other promising fluids are bad actors too, and the most effective ones turn out, almost inevitably, to be the most dangerous.

Theoretically, the most energetic combination is liquid hydrogen and liquid fluorine, which behaves chemically as a super-oxygen. Liquid hydrogen is bad enough, but the mention of liquid fluorine makes the hair of the non-missile chemist stand on end. This fiercely corrosive gas attacks almost every substance with explosive violence, but missile chemists value it for this very violence and dream of the day when they can use it in shipload lots.

Other dangerous but promising fuels are the hydrides of boron. They burn with a green flame and have the unpleasant habit of exploding spontaneously. The missile chemists hope to tame them some day and perhaps use them in combination with liquid fluorine. A missile tearing through the sky freighted with an atom bomb and bunkered with boron hydride and liquid fluorine— its body and wings white hot and its backwash a brilliant green—will be a sight to keep the missile men happy for a long time.

6

MISSILE NEUROPHYSIOLOGY

When a missile is dissected by removing its skin, its brain and other nerve tissue can be spotted easily. The brain is generally found a little behind the nose, just where nature places the brain of most of the higher animals. Its substance, a close-packed mass of tiny vacuum tubes, relays and other electrical components connected together by hair-thin wires, looks remarkably like the microscopic structure of human brain tissue. The vacuum tubes and relays take the place of the neurons (brain cells), and the wires are equivalent to the long thin nerve fibers that join the neurons together.

The missile's brain is much coarser and simpler than

the human brain, which contains several billion inter-connected neurons. It is more like the brain of a very low animal. It works in much the same way—accepting reports from the missile's senses, making decisions on the basis of this information, and sending out orders to the missile's effectors, the electrical or hydraulic motors that control its mechanism. It does this much more rapidly than any animal brain, and it gets reports from much more varied senses.

A missile's brain can be made to respond to light, temperature, acceleration, magnetism, time, direction, radio signals and the speed or density of the outside air. If necessary, it could respond to X-rays coming from the sun, or to cosmic rays coming out of space. It acts on this information in millionths of a second. It can make a thousand decisions while a human brain is pondering a single problem. This flashing speed is necessary. Things happen fast on a missile traveling through the air or space at thousands of miles per hour. An error of direction must be corrected instantaneously or the missile will wander hundreds of miles off course.

In one basic way the missile's brain differs from an animal's brain. The purpose of the brain of even the lowest animal is to preserve the animal's life and help it to grow and reproduce. It makes decisions that move the animal out of danger and toward its food and its mate. The missile's brain, on the other hand, is an in-strument of human policy. It is not concerned with the welfare of the missile; its decisions generally lead the missile only to destruction.

Sometimes human orders are transmitted to the missile's brain over radio channels. Certain ground-to-air missiles, technically known as "beam-riders," are electronically trained to keep close to the center of a radio beam. Once in the air they follow the beam faithfully, and it leads them to the airplane that they will destroy while destroying themselves.

Another type of ground-to-air missile uses a different system. A radar on the ground tracks the enemy bomber. It also tracks the climbing missile and gives it a stream of commands that will bring it to the target.

Most ground-to-air missiles have a homing feature. Their noses contain small radars that search the air with probing pulses. When they feel an aircraft ahead, they tell the missile's brain. It steers the missile on a collision course and explodes the warhead at the most destructive distance.

This behavior is known in missile circles as "the rubber band." Watched on a radarscope, the missile and its victim look like two bright sparks gradually drawing closer. When the rubber band goes into action, they veer together and merge in a single spark. Then little shining points of light flutter to earth slowly.

The earlier ground-to-air missiles were rather stupid. When one of them, for instance, flew toward two airplanes, it could not decide which of them to attack. Its brain went into neurotic oscillations, or it steered a baffled course between the two targets. Modern missiles are more decisive: they no longer make this mistake. It is still difficult, however, to keep them from attacking the falling debris of airplanes that have been blown to pieces by earlier missiles.

Some of the more advanced missiles leave most of their brains behind, carrying in their noses only a token amount of electronic nerve tissue. The complicated reports of the missile's senses are radioed to the ground, where a large brain in a truck or trailer thinks about them instantaneously and radios its conclusions and orders back to the missile in the air. The missile's mechanical muscles obey such orders just as readily as if the decisions had been made by its personal brain.

This system has obvious advantages. Only a minimum of expensive electronic brain tissue is destroyed when the missile explodes, and the great brain squatting on the ground beside its swinging antennae can be much bigger, faster and more intelligent than anything that the missile could carry into the air.

At first glance, this combination of sedentary brain and small, flashing missile many miles away seems odd and novel. But it is not really novel. Nature has used the same system for millions of years in many of its higher evolutionary branches. The advantages of a central brain whose delicate and elaborate bulk is not committed to action were as obvious to nature as to missile-building man.

The tentacles of an octopus, the trunk of an elephant and the human hand are analogous to guided missiles that leave their brains on the ground. When a human hand gropes for an object in darkness and comes lightly in contact with it, the many touch receptors in its finger tips telegraph their reports back to the central brain. The brain analyzes the touch reports and combines them with knowledge that it possesses already, such as the capabilities of the hand's muscles. Then it sends a volley of orders. The muscles of the hand move in unison, and the hand grasps the object that it was groping for.

Guidance systems that use radar to bring a missile to its target have an even more familiar analogue in neurophysiology. The action of the human hand in picking up a pencil that the eyes can see is accomplished by the same guiding sequence. First the eyes (the body's radar) observe the pencil and measure its direction and distance. The brain analyzes these reports and tells the hand (the missile) to move in the pencil's general direction. The eyes watch both pencil and hand, and the brain sends out a stream of orders that makes the two move closer together. When the finger tips reach the pencil, the brain receives touch reports as well as sight reports. Acting quickly upon this new information, it tells the hand to grasp the pencil firmly.

Long-range missiles that send back reports from their radar or television eyes also use a distant brain. In their case the brain belongs to the human operator who watches the television screen and steers the missile by what he sees upon it. Only missiles that steer by the stars do all of their own thinking.

Even these depend to some extent on the thinking of other brains. They are like ships' officers who shoot the stars with a sextant and then find their position by consulting tables of figures in a nautical almanac. The navigator might derive those figures himself, but the effort would be enormous. It is much simpler to take advantage of the crystallized thinking of past generations of navigators.

Far-flying missiles that steer by the stars will do something similar. They will carry in their brains on magnetic tape or photographic film figures to help them to find their position from the bearings of the stars. If they are sensitive to the earth's magnetic field, they will carry tables to represent its changes of directon and intensity.

Besides such tables of figures, long-range missiles will carry instructions roughly equivalent to the sealed orders that the captains of old-time sailing ships were commanded to open after they had cleared their ports. These orders will tell the missile where to go and what target to hit. They will probably give it detailed instructions about how to burn its fuel to the best advantage, how to climb to altitude and how to descend in a long glide to its final target.

The designing of electronic brains is one of the most exciting fields of modern technology. The neurophysiologists who work with nerve tissue of metal, plastic and glass cover the whole range from practical gadgetmakers to logicians and philosophers. Most of them try hard to keep their excitement down, protesting that they are merely developing unusually complicated circuits. Few of them really believe it.

As soon as they fall off guard, an excited tone lights

up their conversation. They speak of the elaborate apparatuses that they are creating as if they had living personalities. They rejoice in their machines' intellectual accomplishments with all the the pride of parents applauding their child's report card. When one of their electronic brains functions really well, they fall in love with it like Pygmalion, who carved a block of marble into human flesh. Then they recover indignantly and point out that the most elaborate electronic brain is nothing but a servo-mechanism that obeys human commands. Next moment, off guard again, they call their machine by pet names and revel in its intelligence.

The success of guided missiles and of the space vehicles that are their extension depends very largely upon the ingenuity of the electronic neurophysiologists. Rockets that take off from the earth headed into space will have to fly themselves during the critical early stages of their ascent, when enormous acceleration forces will keep human brains from functioning. Even if they were working well, human brains would not be fast enough to control the rocket properly. It will need an electronic brain to absorb reports from dozens of specialized senses and act upon them in micro-seconds with no errors at all.

When the rocket reaches the comparative calm of space and time becomes more plentiful, the human brains on board will still be inadequate. To guide a space ship among the planets is a bewilderingly complicated mathematical problem. The ship's position must first be determined by observing the stars. Then its curving course must be plotted with extreme accuracy. This is only a beginning; selecting a future course through space toward the chosen objective is even more difficult.

The position and orbit of the objective—say Mars—must be considered. Since the gravitational fields of the earth, the moon and the sun will affect the course, they must all be located accurately in relation to the ship. Each of these factors introduces a cloud of figures. Astronomers accustomed to working out such problems demand months for each job. A space ship's captain must have the answers in minutes. Human brains do not work fast enough; only a great electronic brain that can absorb information direct from the navigating telescopes and digest it instantaneously can hope to keep the space ship on its desired course.

Such brains exist at present, but they are sedentary monsters, much too heavy and fragile. They would fill the whole space ship and absorb all its power supply. They would surely be wrecked by the crushing thrust of its rocket motor.

During the first few critical minutes of a space ship's ascent, the bulk of its thinking might be done, as in the case of some guided missiles, by computing apparatus on the ground. The reading of the ship's instruments would flow to the computer over radio channels, and the solutions and signals of command would flow back to the ship. But eventually the ship must rise beyond the reach of such apron strings. Then it will need an independent brain light enough to be carried and tough enough to survive the jolt of departure.

A few years ago the electronic neurophysiologists saw little hope of constructing such a brain. Each design that promised to show the necessary intelligence demanded thousands upon thousands of vacuum tubes, each of which occupied a considerable space and called for electric current to heat its glowing filament. Each performed the functions of a single neuron in an animal brain, and even the brains of very simple animals need hundreds of thousands of neurons.

A recent development, the transistor, has cheered the brain designers. With transistors it is possible, theoretically at least, to construct brains that are light and tough but still intelligent enough to do all the tasks that may be required of them.

Transistors are specks of germanium, a rare element found in odd places such as the flue dust of gasworks and the refuse left over from zinc refining. When crystallized in a careful and special way and cut into pieces the size of a strawberry seed, germanium can be made to perform nearly all the functions of a vacuum tube. It demands almost no current and generates almost no heat. When sealed into a solid block of plastic, a battery of transistors is tough enough to be fired from a cannon without being damaged at all.

When the electronic brain-makers talk about transistors, their eyes light up as if they'd seen a vision. Transistors need not be appreciably bigger than neurons and they can think a thousand times faster. There is no theoretical reason why a transistorized brain should not be as intelligent as a human brain with all its billions of neurons and still not be too big for a space ship to carry.

At this point, the electronic neurophysiologists sometimes get lost in philosophical questions. Can man, they ask, construct a brain more intelligent than his own? Some authorities believe that the human brain has qualities that no mechanism can equal or exceed. Others see no limit ahead—pointing out that electronic brains can already solve mathematical problems beyond human reach.

They also point out that human brains can join in co-operating groups. In large research centers, for instance, each human brain contributes some specially trained ability. Electronic brains can co-operate too, growing in intellectual capacity as new parts are added. Eventually, say these optimists, the non-human research center can outstrip the collective intelligence of the entire faculty of the Massachusetts Institute of Technology. It will be more dependable too, for its parts will not die, or sabotage one another, or move to California or go into the advertising business. When such a brain swings into action, it will act like the central intelligence of a multi-celled animal. It will have a purpose of its own, ruling the men who created it as the brain of a man rules the cells of his body.

Such philosophical problems are not the immediate concern of the electronic neurophysiologists. Transistors are hard to manufacture, and the problem of connecting them in the properly intricate way by means of fine wires no bigger than strands of silk has not yet been solved. The dream of a transistorized brain that can outthink a thousand Einsteins is something for the distant future.

Brains for missiles or space ships are a great deal simpler. Their designers like to point out that a trained human being, such as the navigator or the pilot of an air liner, uses only a small part of his brain in performing his professional functions. When he works out his position from radio signals or the readings of a bubble sextant, he may sweat and furrow his brow, but most of the neurons in his brain are idling.

A great many more of them come into play when he goes off duty and writes a letter to his girl. This project activates billions of neurons—including those billions concerned with language, with social conventions, with complicated personal memories and with deep instincts far older than the human race.

An electronic computer at M.I.T. that could write a productive love letter to its electronic girl friend at Caltech is out of the question at present, but a specialized, limited brain that can fly a rocket or space ship may have been constructed already. The electronic nervous systems of jet interceptors are not far from this goal.

In these semi-human mechanisms the pilot goes along only for the ride. His duties are to nurse the ship into the air and bring it back to earth after the completion of its mission. Radars on the ground steer the interceptor to the general vicinity of the target—a high-flying enemy bomber. Then the interceptor's own brain takes over, guides it closer to the target, figures out the proper course for interception, fires the guns or air-to-air rockets at the proper distance and bounces the interceptor upward to avoid the falling debris. The pilot goes into action after this electronic spasm and takes charge again, flying the ship (with what composure he can muster) back to its base.

These semi-automatic interceptors are already guarding the coasts and outposts of the United States. They are regarded as temporary expedients, soon to be replaced by completely automatic interceptors with no pilots at all. The chief obstacles to this development are the size, weight and fragility of the electronic apparatus that they must carry. When transistors are perfected and manufactured in quantity, the interceptors' thinking apparatus will shrink to one-tenth or one-hundredth of its present size. The automatic interceptors will then be guided missiles that are intelligent enough to destroy their targets without destroying themselves.

From this point, which may have been reached already, it will be comparatively easy to build a brain intelligent enough to fly a rocket into space and guide it by the stars on a course to the moon. The function of the crew, if any, will be to deal with unforeseen emergencies.

7

STEPS GOING UP

The nightmare technology of missiles described in the preceding chapters is the soil from which true space flight must grow. Like the real soil underfoot, it is wildly complex. It is also mysterious because nearly all of its facts dive underground into military secrecy or fray out into rumors.

Each test range or development center is a source of rumors that spread like ripples, gradually losing with distance any content of accuracy that they may have contained. The flying-saucer hallucination may be attributed, in part, to the public's conviction that all sorts of strange objects are flying through the sky. In this belief the public may be right. It is likely that some missiles are already flying fast enough to shine in the dark. They may have colored exhausts, and they may fly very differently from conventional aircraft.

The mystery that surrounds guided missiles is also responsible for the widespread popular conviction that true space flight is just around the corner. It is hard for the missile men to discuss this matter in detail without violating their oaths of secrecy. Most of them agree, however, that true space flight will not spring overnight, like a mushroom, from the swarming soil of missile technology. It will have to grow slowly and for years, like a tall tree. "Just look at the space-flight problems," the missile men advise. "You can see for yourself how difficult it is."

The best way to visualize space as a navigable medium is to think of it as a smooth and waveless lake. Most of its surface is glassy smooth, and floating objects like chips or dead leaves can drift across it easily, propelled by the gentlest forces. But widely scattered over it are deep, sucking whirlpools like the eddies that form above the intakes of powerhouse penstocks. These are the gravitational fields of the sun or the planets. At a distance their suction is weak to the vanishing point, but at close range it increases sharply.

A space-borne body such as an asteroid, a comet or a space ship can skim across the voids as easily as a floating leaf on the surface of a pond. It feels only faintly the pull of the distant whirlpools, but if it comes near one of them, a mighty force takes hold of it, like the unseen spirit that gripped the keel of the ship of the

Ancient Mariner. Faster and faster it races toward the sucking whirlpool; stronger and stronger grows the force that pulls it down.

The ultimate fate of a body in the clutch of a gravitational whirlpool depends on its original speed as it sailed across untroubled space. If it was moving fast enough, it will probably escape. The whirlpool will deflect it from its original course, but will not capture it. This is what happens to most of the comets that plunge toward the sun from cold outer space. Long before they come close to the sun, they develop tremendous speed. So unless they make a direct hit on the sun, they will whip around it and shoot outward again, damaged and diminished, into the depths of space.

Slower-moving bodies with less speed to save them are not as fortunate. They are dragged down the plunging side of the gravitational whirlpool and captured by the hungry mass that waits for them at the bottom. This is what happens to luckless meteors that die in a streak of light when they hit the earth's atmosphere.

The cardinal principle of space navigation is to keep far away from gravitational whirlpools. In the placid ocean of emptiness, very small forces will steer a space ship and waft it from course to course. But unfortunately for space navigators, they must start their voyages from the very bottom of a powerful sucking whirlpool, the strong gravitational field that surrounds the earth. Before they can reach the easy sailing of untroubled space, they must make a tremendous effort to escape from the earth's grip. They are like ships that are separated from a wide, placid ocean by a violent storm raging inside their harbor.

Rocket men can figure easily how much energy must be expended to battle through the initial storm of the earth's gravitational field. Expressed in speed, it is 25,000 miles per hour. This is not fast on the astronomical scale. Many meteors hit the earth's atmosphere at 140,000 miles per hour, and the earth itself swings around its orbit at 66,600 miles per hour. But measured by existing human standards, 25,000 miles per hour is fast. It is ten times as fast as a rifle bullet and about thirty-five times as fast as a jet fighter. Rocket men have agreed that no single-stage rocket can reach such a speed.

The trouble with a single-stage rocket is that its payload is its entire structure, including its motor, pumps, tanks, fuselage and control apparatus. Even with perfect theoretical efficiency the energy in the rocket's fuel is not sufficient to accelerate this considerable mass to the necessary speed. Some additional trick is needed to shoot a rocket or a space ship free of the earth's gravitation.

Long before World War II, the rocket men worked out a promising trick: the two-stage rocket. This is a large rocket with a smaller one fixed in its nose. The large rocket fires first. When it has reached the peak of its speed and its fuel is about gone, the second rocket fires. It is full of fuel but is already moving rapidly. It starts its upward flight like a fresh relay runner and so reaches much greater speed than a single-stage rocket could.

The most optimistic rocket men believe that a two-stage rocket might possibly reach the critical speed of 25,000 miles per hour. Some of their colleagues are not as hopeful. They believe that a three-stage rocket will be required, and that even this complicated vehicle cannot carry much payload out of the earth's gravitational whirlpool.

The trouble with multi-stage rockets is that each stage must be enormously larger than the stage above it. To toss even a jeep-sized payload into placid space, a three-stage rocket would have to be as big as an ocean liner. So the resourceful rocket men have thought of a second trick. Instead of making their escape from the earth in one breathless swoop, they propose to construct a resting place partway up the side of the whirlpool.

The best way to think about this project is to imagine that the earth, like the moon, has no atmosphere; then imagine a rocket fired horizontally from the peak of a high mountain. If its speed is no greater than that of existing rockets, it will be dragged down to the earth's surface only a few dozen miles from its launching point. If its speed is increased, it will fly farther and farther before the earth's pull curves it down to the surface. Eventually it will reach a speed that keeps it exactly parallel to the curvature of the earth. Unless it happens to hit another mountain, it will skim all the way around the earth and return to its launching place.

During this trip, the circumnavigating rocket is falling all the time toward the center of the earth. But its own speed, tending to shoot it outward in a straight line, is exactly enough to counteract its falling motion. The resulting curve is a circular orbit just above the earth's surface. The speed necessary to maintain a vehicle in such an orbit is 17,000 miles per hour, considerably less than the "escape velocity" of 25,000 miles per hour.

At greater distances from the earth, even less speed is necessary. A vehicle moving on an orbit one thousand miles above the earth need travel at only 16,000 miles per hour. At this speed it will pass around the earth once every two hours and will do this indefinitely without expenditure of energy. It will be like the moon, which needs no rocket motor to keep it revolving in its orbit.

The figures of orbital motion are comforting to space men. It takes considerably less energy to reach an orbit than it does to escape from the earth into the high seas of space. But when they lay plans to place a space ship in a suitable orbit, they find themselves involved in complex mathematics. Firing a rocket upward at an angle like a cannon shell is no good. If left to itself, it will follow an elliptical course around the earth's center of gravitation. Since it started at a point on the surface of the earth, it will return and hit another point on the surface of the earth. To avoid this eventuality, the rocket must make a turn, high above the atmosphere, and put itself into a circular course that will not bring it back to the earth.

This maneuver requires energy supplied by the rocket's fuel. So does the long upward flight against the earth's gravitation. So does the effort to reach the necessary speed in the chosen orbit. But all three expenditures of energy added together come to a figure that is moderate enough to encourage the space men. They believe that a multi-stage rocket of reasonable dimensions (by their liberal standards) can set a profitable payload revolving permanently in a stable orbit.

From this point their theorizing becomes almost plain sailing. They propose to send up rocket after rocket, each leaving a payload in the same orbit. The payloads will consist of parts and supplies for a satellite station designed to operate in a vacuum far from the earth. When enough of the payloads have accumulated in the orbit, the station can be put together, stocked with supplies and manned with a crew. It will circle in its orbit round and round the earth and can be used as a base for more ambitious operations.

Skeptics are apt to point out that an orbit a thousand miles above the earth's surface is still a long way away from Mars, or even from the moon. The space men are ready for this comment and pounce on it eagerly. The halfway station traveling in its orbit, they point out, has already won the worst of its battle with the earth's gravitational field; it is now moving around the earth at 16,000 miles per hour. A long-range space ship, constructed and outfitted at the station and moving around with it on its rapid orbit, needs only a small additional push (about 7,000 miles per hour) to escape from the earth entirely. It can be built in any desired size and supplied with the necessary fuel. Its parts, supplies and crew can be brought up, little by little, by shuttle rockets from the earth. While the long-range space ship is being assembled, the satellite station will be a valuable training place for crews preparing themselves for longer space voyages.

Most of the men who think about satellite stations, space ships, and voyages to the moon or the planets have no immediate hope of putting their theories into practice. They are merely enjoying those semi-material dreams that entertain technological man, just as dreams of Nirvana or Paradise entertained religious man before technology developed. But a few of these modern-style mystics are really in earnest. The most prominent of them is Dr. Wernher von Braun (of the V-2s) whose serious proposal for reaching space is worth detailed attention.

8

SPACE CRUSADE

Dr. Wernher von Braun is an unusual example of the sub-species *homo technologicus*. There is no doubt about his engineering competence. He reels off tight-linked figures and formulae as if he were a baseball fan leaning on a bar and repeating batting averages. His record confirms this impression. The German V-2 rocket project of which he was head and inspiration proved fantastically successful. It started with nothing but Professor Goddard's embryonic liquid-fuel rocket. In a few years of furious work, it produced the horrendous V-2, which still has the admiration of present-day rocket men.

But von Braun is more than a mere technician; he is also something of a prophet and something of a mystic. He is regarded by the more conventional rocket men with the mixture of suspicion and admiration that must have been felt by cozily established clerics toward Saint Francis of Assisi or Peter the Hermit. He worries and frightens them with his technological visions. When he talks to the lay public about his confident plans for voyaging into space, they accuse him of preaching to the birds. When they observe the following that has gathered around him of little boys in toy-shop space suits and teen-age enthusiasts with space dust in their eyes, they accuse him of leading a children's crusade toward sure disappointment.

Von Braun's reply to this criticism is much like that which Peter the Hermit must have given to the abbots and bishops who deplored his disquieting influence. "Enthusiasm and faith," says von Braun, "are necessary ingredients of every great project. Prophets have always been laughed at, deplored and opposed, but some prophets have proved to be following the true course of history."

Von Braun's satellite station proposal, which he calls "a prelude to space flight," sounds as fantastic as the children's crusade preached by Peter the Hermit. But Peter the Hermit was right in a sense. If medieval Europe could have got together and exerted its unified force against the infidels, it might just possibly have won the crusade. On this large scale of reference, von Braun may be right too.

The first step toward space, says von Braun, will be to build a fleet of three-stage rockets, each weighing

7,000 tons when loaded with fuel, and standing 240 feet high. This is somewhat less than the weight of a modern light cruiser. The 51 rocket motors in the first stage will have a combined thrust of 14,000 tons, which is equivalent to the thrust of 6,000 of the jet engines that are used in modern fighters. When fired, they will move the rocket upward with an initial acceleration of 1 G. That is as fast as a falling body increases its speed in the earth's gravitational field. As the fuel in the tanks is consumed, the rocket becomes lighter. Since the thrust of the motors remains the same, the acceleration increases swiftly to 9 Gs.

The motors will fire for 84 seconds, burning 5,250 tons of fuel; then the first stage of the rocket, empty and exhausted, falls back toward earth. The second stage, which fits into the forward end of the first stage, weighs 990 tons. Its motors, which have 1,750 tons of thrust, start firing immediately and burn for 124 seconds. Then the second stage drops off exhausted, leaving the final third stage, which contains the crew and controls and cargo, alone on its flight into space. This final stage, which weights 143 tons all told, is the part that will reach the orbit and park its payload there. It has wings to help it return to earth safely.

Von Braun's great three-stage rocket, of course, will not fly directly upward. If it did, it would fall back to earth not far from its launching point. It starts upward vertically, but is turned toward the east by automatic controls while it is still in the atmosphere where its rudders can grip the air. Turning toward the east is important and so is a launching site near the earth's equator. All objects on the earth's surface near the equator are carried toward the east by the earth's revolution at one thousand miles per hour. This considerable speed, which costs nothing, is important in the calculations of the space navigators. If the rocket were to take off toward the west or from a point nearer one of the poles, it would have to use more fuel to reach the desired orbit.

Von Braun's rocket rises in its eastward curve until it attains the altitude of 24.9 miles. At this point it is moving almost horizontally at a speed of 1.46 miles per second or 5,256 miles per hour. The second stage then separates and continues to climb gradually, keeping within the outer fringe of the atmosphere where steering is still possible. After 124 seconds of powered flight, it has reached the altitude of forty miles and is moving at 14,364 miles per hour. The winged third stage uses its motors for 84 seconds, reaching an altitude of 63.3 miles and a speed of 18,468 miles per hour.

The motors are cut off before their fuel supply is wholly exhausted. The rocket's speed is then sufficient to place it on an elliptical orbit that rises higher and higher above the surface of the earth. During this rise, the pull of the earth's gravitation reduces the speed of the rocket. When it has reached the altitude of 1,075 miles above the surface, it is moving only 14,770 miles per hour. This condition is unstable. The rocket has not quite enough speed to keep it in its orbit, and it is moving not in a circle but in an ellipse which will carry it eventually back to the surface of the earth.

Up to this point the rocket's flight was programmed automatically. Even von Braun, who has the self-confidence of a Teutonic demigod, does not believe that any crew can function effectively under the strains of the roaring ascent. So clever and complicated instruments will have to keep the rocket on its course through the thinning air and detach the first two stages at the proper moments. But when the third stage is clear of the earth's atmosphere and is approaching the high point of its ascending ellipse, the crew will be called upon for complicated action. Its members may rejoice to be in control of their ship, but they cannot relax and enjoy the novel sensation of space flight. They will have too much to do. They must counter by appropriate action all the errors that may have accumulated during the automatic ascent of the three-stage rocket.

By use of instruments and astronomical observations, they will check the position, course and speed of their ship. Then by means of gyroscopes or small flywheels spinning in its innards, they will point its nose in the direction of the desired orbit. When the heading is correct, they will turn on the rocket's motors for 15 seconds, increasing its speed to 15,840 miles per hour. This is the critical speed needed to keep the ship in a circular orbit 1,075 miles above the surface of the earth. Then the men can relax, if they are in a mood to do so. Their unpowered ship will cruise forever, round and round the earth like a small moon.

Probably the crew men will not feel like relaxation; the worst part of their trip still lies ahead. They will unload their cargo (sections of the satellite station) and park it in space. It will not fall, of course, or fall behind. If not pushed out of the rocket too hard, it will follow obediently on the orbit, each piece like another small moon.

It is almost certain that the crew will have carried into space a collection of rabbit's feet, St. Christopher medals and other magical talismen from the pre-technological past. These will be invoked at that terrible moment when the rocket starts down toward the earth.

The earth below will look peaceful enough. The men will see whole countries and continents, mottled with green and brown and flecked with the bright white of clouds. They may follow the shorelines and search for familiar places where they once lived, but each man will realize clearly that a frightful ordeal lies between him and the peaceful surface.

Most of the energy generated by the combustion of 7,000 tons of fuel has been packed in the form of speed and altitude in their small rocket, and this must all be dissipated before it can come to rest. If the ship were to plunge directly down toward the earth, friction with the air would turn it into a fireball trailing a stream of flame. If any solid portions should manage to struggle down to the hard surface, they would flash on impact into a white-hot gas. A chemical analysis of the soil where the rocket had struck would probably be needed to detect any traces of it.

Von Braun admits that careful maneuvering will be required to avoid this eventuality. His third-stage rocket has strong swept-back wings, and he proposes to reach the earth safely by flying through the fringe of the atmosphere and using it as a brake. Friction between the skin and the scattered air molecules will turn the rocket's energy gradually into heat. The heat will dissipate, and the rocket will slow to the manageable speed of an ordinary airplane.

To start this ticklish maneuver, the men in the rocket will turn their craft so that the exhausts of its motors point directly ahead of its motion in the circling orbit. They will let the motors blast for just long enough to reduce the speed by 1,070 miles per hour. After this power maneuver, the rocket will no longer be moving fast enough to stay in a stable orbit. It will be in a descending ellipse that will carry it in a gentle curve down toward the edge of the atmosphere.

The curving fall will last for 51 minutes, and the pull of gravitation will increase the rocket's speed to 18,500 miles per hour. This speed is so great that if the rocket were to miss the atmosphere, it would rush past the earth and soar outward in an ellipse on the other side. The same would happen if the rocket were in the position normal to flying aircraft. As soon as its wings met the atmosphere they would exert an upward lift which would bounce the rocket out again into empty space.

So the pilot (von Braun admits that he must be an unusually skillful pilot) takes care that the rocket enters the atmosphere upside down, with its wings exerting a downward pressure as they react with the air. This keeps the rocket on a curving course inside the atmosphere, so that it can be slowed by air resistance.

Heat will develop immediately and make the rocket and its wings glow a bright cherry red. The pilot will have to watch not only the normal airplane instruments, but also a baleful row of dials that report the temperature of the wings and other surfaces. If the temperature rises too high, their metals will soften and lose their streamlined shape. Air resistance will increase, and temperature will rise higher. The rocket will turn in an instant into a fireball.

But if all goes well, the pilot balances his speed against his outside temperature. When the wings get too hot, he will ease off a little, taking his ship up to air that is thinner and does not generate quite as much heat. If the temperature falls lower than the wings can stand, he ventures a little deeper into the atmosphere.

Von Braun figures that the temperature should be held to about 1300° F. This is far above the softening point of metals now used in aircraft, but von Braun believes that special heat-resisting alloys can stand it without softening. He insists that such alloys can be applied to the outer skin of the rocket and its wings in such a way that little of the heat that is developed in them will penetrate to the interior. The heat that does penetrate can be stopped short of the cabin by proper insulation. The rocket's windows will be made of heat-resistant glass and will be cooled by circulating liquids to keep them from fusing.

Around the earth the rocket will coast, part meteor, part airplane. As its speed diminishes, it can safely venture into thicker air. At some point in the slowing process, it will turn over, so that its wings will support it instead of holding it down. At last its speed will diminish to that of a normal airplane. It will fly at moderate altitude, powered if necessary by gentle blasts from its rocket motors, and land at its base no faster than an air liner. The crew will de-rocket, perhaps a little shaken. While they drink Coca-Colas in the space pilots' club or write letters to their girls, their ship will be fueled and checked for another trip to the orbit.

This is only a brief summary of von Braun's proposal, which he has been developing in elaborate detail since before he started working on the V-2s in Germany. He regards some parts as tentative. He is hopeful, for instance, that the bulky first stages of the rocket, which are shucked off during the early parts of the flight, can be recovered undamaged and used again. He suggests that the launching site be selected so that the first few hundred miles of the ascent will be over open ocean. The exhausted first- and second-stage rockets will fall toward the sea, braked during their descent by steel-mesh parachutes. As they approach the water, solid-fuel rockets in their noses will fire, further slowing their fall and easing them into the sea with (says von Braun) only minor damage.

Then special ships built like floating drydocks and guided by radar will hurry to pick them up and carry them back to the launching site to be used again. Von

Braun is confident that the first stages can be recovered, but he is not sure that it will be practical to do so. He admits that building and operating the recovery ships may be more expensive than it would be to build new first and second stages for each shuttle to the orbit. This part of his program, he believes, will have to be evaluated in a strictly economic manner to keep the cost of the whole project down to a modest $4,000,000,000.

9

SATELLITE STATION

Even the expansive von Braun admits that these flights to the orbit will be an enormous enterprise. They will require an elaborate base, probably on an oceanic island, which will amount to a sizable and highly specialized city. Besides the launching site itself, as dangerous during an ascent as an erupting volcano, there will have to be laboratories, machine shops, testing facilities, residential quarters at a safe distance and a vast network of sharp-eyed, unwinking instruments. There will be a great tank farm for the dangerous fuels and a port for the tankers that will bring them to the island. Back in the home country, presumably the United States, will be the special chemical factories to produce the fuels. The touchy and hostile liquids that von Braun proposes to use (hydrazine and fuming nitric acid) are not manufactured at present in sufficient quantity. To supply them will require a new and enormous industry.

Back in the home country, too, will be schools to train the men who will fly the rockets and the technicians who will ready them for their trips to the orbit. Von Braun does not anticipate much trouble with recruitment. He is probably right about this; danger gilded with glory has little power to repel. If his crusade into space to capture the technical Holy Grail ever gets under way, it will surely attract plenty of young men who hunger for gilded danger.

This has always been so. The armored knights of the Middle Ages who set out for Jerusalem knew that their chances of returning were, by the record, small. Three centuries later, few Spanish adventurers returned from their New World conquests, but Cortez and Pizarro got plenty of volunteers.

All this great enterprise, centering on an island that will erupt periodically with white-hot flames, is pointed toward a physically small result. Each 7,000-ton rocket will carry up to the orbit only 36 tons of payload. It will be like the laborious process of infusing and distilling droplets of oil of roses out of tons of rose petals. But oil of roses sells at a profit, and von Braun believes that each small deposit of gear in the high orbit will be profitable too. He figures that about fifteen trips from the surface of the earth will be needed to carry up all the parts of a permanent satellite station.

As he tells about setting up this station, his blue eyes glow like those of a Teutonic warlock from the days of the elder Edda, but his lips speak the hard-shelled phrases of modern technological prophecy. He and his fellow-enthusiasts, chiefly German, American and British, have dreamed for many years about their inhabited artificial moon, and they have given loving attention to every conceivable detail.

It will be a strange habitation, this fragile bubble in space supported against gravitation on a swinging trapeze of speed. All conditions on board will be novel. Instead of shedding rain, the satellite's roof will have to shed a patter of microscopic meteorites. The air inside will be artificial, probably a mixture of oxygen and helium. Drinking water must be recycled; the vapor that comes from human lungs and human perspiration will be condensed and purified for re-use. Even friendly gravitation will be totally absent unless created artificially.

It is this observer's opinion that the lonely satellite under the cold black sky will have one familiar item. The magnesium or plastic walls of the crew's quarters will be thickly papered with pictures of naked women. There is precedent for this. The most austere cloisters of technological man display these proofs of biological conservatism. They smile and wriggle above the drawing boards of airplane designers, among the massed instruments in roaring test facilities, even close to those scientific shrines: the cyclotrons and nuclear reactors of the atomic physicists. A large and very naked example faces the door of an instrument trailer operated by the rocket men of Caltech.

This near-universal practice has been noted by philosophical technologists, and a good deal of semi-playful thought has been applied to it. Most of the theorists agree that the pinup girls are needed relief for human spirits that are subconsciously oppressed by the sight of too many non-human hands, senses and brains. They are comforting reminders that one human function, reproduction, has resisted mechanization and will probably retain indefinitely its traditional features.

Some theorists go further. Reproduction, they say, often looks back nostalgically to an earlier stage of evolution. The ancient fish that crawled out of the sea to become man's ancestors must have had similar, though dimmer, nostalgic emotions. They were amphibious like modern toads. They spent most of their time on land, but when the season came for their reproduction, they returned to their ancestral water and there performed the joyful function of continuing their species. The first men who take up life in the hostile medium of space will be "amphibious" too. When they wish to reproduce, they will return to the comfortable earth to rendezvous with the pin-ups.

Aside from the nostalgic pinups and the atavistic rabbits' feet in the space men's pockets, little in the satellite station will be familiar. The principal cause of this novelty is the lack of gravitation. Since the station is a satellite moving on its own orbit, its inhabitants will not feel the earth's gravitation. They will be like inhabitants of the moon (if any existed), who feel the pull of the moon itself but do not feel the pull of the earth around which the moon is revolving. The mass of the satellite station is too small to exert perceptible gravitation, so its inhabitants will feel none whatever.

This weightlessness has some advantages. The satellite must retain an atmosphere with a pressure of at least ten pounds per square inch, so its walls will have to be fairly strong and will have to have a shape that resists outward pressure. But the rest of it need have little strength. The interior floors and walls can be made extremely thin. Under conditions of weightlessness even the most massive objects, such as tanks of water and stocks of supplies, will not press heavily against them, and the feet of the human crews will flick across their surfaces as lightly as the feet of flies.

Lack of gravitation will have strange effects on life and housekeeping on the satellite. Liquids, for instance, will not flow through pipes unless they are pushed by positive pressure. No object will remain in place unless it is fastened firmly. A slight push exerted against a large piece of equipment will send it moving slowly but steadily to the far end of the room. The air will not circulate by means of convection currents, for warm air will not be lighter than cold air. Around each man, for instance, a mass of vitiated air from his lungs will slowly accumulate. Fresh air from the purifying system will not penetrate of its own accord to all parts of the ship. It will have to be forced into every cranny by means of carefully contrived fans and pressurized ducts.

The most bizarre effect of lack of gravity will be on the crew themselves. Men normally get around by pushing against the friction between the soles of their feet and the floor beneath them. On the space station, their bodies will have no weight and will therefore create no friction. A backward-pressing foot will get less traction than if it were on wet ice, and as soon as a foot presses down with the action that normally creates friction, the man's body will rise from the floor and continue rising until his head hits an obstacle.

The crew of a space station without gravitation will have to move around by pulling themselves carefully from handhold to handhold. At first they may enjoy this sensation of floating through the air, as in space movies, but soon they will learn that free floating is hard on both bodies and equipment.

They can sleep anywhere, of course; their bodies will not feel the hardest surface beneath them. But they will not enjoy this sleeping on air that is softer than the fluffiest mattress. As soon as they are asleep, the jet effect of the breath from their nostrils will propel them across the room until their heads fetch up against a solid wall. They will learn to prefer bunks, where restraining straps will protect them from involuntary sleep-floating.

Heavy objects can be moved with ease, and chairs need not be padded, but most space architects believe that some gravitation will make life on the satellite station much more pleasant for the crew. So nearly all designs of space stations include a provision for creating a small but sufficient amount of synthetic gravitation.

This can be done by making the station revolve slowly. Then the crew will feel the same centrifugal force that is enjoyed by kids riding on a merry-go-round. It is not exactly gravitation, but is connected with it through the difficult abstractions of Einstein's relativity. So far as humans can tell, the effect is just the same. As soon as the station starts spinning, their bodies will have weight again and will attempt to move toward the outermost walls, just as objects on the surface of the earth attempt to move inward toward the earth's center.

"Down" for the spacemen will be outward, and "up" will be inward toward the station's center of revolution. Loose objects will stay in place. Smoke, if smoking is permitted, will rise (inward) from the tips of their cigarettes. Water will circulate through the pipes, and the crew can sleep strapless in their bunks without fear of drifting off.

For the crew it will be a grand moment when the gravity is turned on. Their viscera will settle in place against the pouch of their bellies. They can walk again without fear that their skulls will hit the ceiling. Their coffee will stay in its cups, and all the miscellaneous objects—pencils, clothing and displaced globules of soup—that have been circulating in the cabin will settle to the floor. The men will sit down at their desks with relief and radio to their girls on earth that life in a space station is not so bad after all.

The design of space stations has been governed largely

by the desirability of synthesizing gravitation, combined with the necessity of retaining air pressure with the least possible weight. The simplest form that fills these two needs would be a sphere, but spheres are impractical. The greater part of their inhabitable space is close to the axis of revolution where no gravity is felt. A man who climbs upward (inward) through the dead spot will meet gravity pulling at him from the opposite direction. Both his feet and head will be "down." Space architects agree that this experience is apt to be upsetting.

A more frequent, if less picturesque cause of trouble will be the great fluctuation in gravity between the "equator" of the space station and its interior. The pseudo-gravity of spinning will be felt most strongly in the parts that are moving most rapidly. Elsewhere its pull will be much weaker. So every movable object in a spherical space station will have sharply fluctuating weight. Instruments and equipment will work differently in different places, and men are apt to forget under what gravitational regime they are operating at the moment.

Space architects, abandoning the sphere, have turned to a form of space station that is almost entirely equator. It will be shaped like a doughnut or an inner tube and will be made of strong gas-tight fabric kept tightly inflated by the pressure of its synthetic atmosphere. It will revolve like a wheel around an axis passing through its hub.

The wheel design has many advantages. Since most of the station's enclosed space is near the outer edge, the pseudo-gravitational field will be reasonably uniform. The walls will not have to be rigid; they will be supported by air pressure only. Access to the station will be through tubes leading to the hub, which will be turning slowly but not moving sideways.

There is no more fascinating game than space-station architecture. Anyone with a modicum of technical knowledge can get into the act, and many men who have little do get into it. The literature of this subject contains an enormous amount of ingenious doodling. No space station has been built, even for practice on the ground, but considerable thought has been given to such unlikely subjects as disposal of garbage and space gardening. A book containing all the bright ideas would be lots of fun, but too heavy to handle.

The space garbage problem, for instance, was solved by Willy Ley, an entertaining science writer who has made space flight one of his special fields, and has written several all-out books on the subject. Garbage and other undesired material, Ley points out, cannot be merely ejected from the satellite. It will follow the station on its orbit like a homeless but hopeful dog. Each water molecule and larger particle in its volatile material will select an orbit of its own closely paralleling the orbit of the ship. Soon the ship will be surrounded by a thin but faithful cloud of disseminated garbage. This retinue will be annoying, and it will spoil the sharpness of astronomical observation.

So Willy Ley proposes to enclose the refuse as it accumulates in light aluminum containers, each provided with a small rocket. When a container is full, it will be shot backward along the orbit, thus destroying part of its speed. It will now be in a descending ellipse and will separate from the space station. Down it will swing in a long flat curve toward the waiting earth. When it encounters the atmosphere at 18,000 miles an hour, it will slow and plunge steeply into it. The undesirable material, incinerated by speed, will be scattered by the garbage meteor through hundreds of miles of air as novel but inoffensive gases.

A more vital problem is power supply to run the elaborate equipment that will be needed on the space station. Conventional fuel such as gasoline is out of the question. It would have to be carried up from the earth with enormous effort and would need imported oxygen to make it burn. Other chemical fuels are no more promising; they will all be too heavy to carry into the orbit in sufficient quantity. So most space designers favor the use of sunlight, which is much stronger in space than it is at the bottom of the atmosphere and can be depended upon except when the station is in the shadow of the earth.

Nearly all the designs employ some sort of concave mirror to concentrate the rays of the sun on a boiler containing water, mercury, or some other "working fluid." The fluid will vaporize and pass through turbines to generate power; then it will go to condensers in the cold shadow on the sunless side of the space station. There it will turn into a liquid to be returned to the boiler.

There is much argument in interplanetary circles about whether this arrangement can work well enough. The energy source is no problem; a great abundance of heat can be extracted from the powerful and constant sunlight. The big problem is the condenser. The effectiveness of all such engines depends upon the contrast between the temperature in their boilers and that in their condensers. The trouble with condensers in space is that they can keep themselves cool only by radiating their heat away. There is no air to blow through them, as in the cooling systems of automobiles.

Unfortunately, the shaded parts of a satellite station are not always particularly cold, nowhere near as cold as they would be in a part of space that is far from the earth. The surface of the earth below the space station is often in sunlight too, and it reflects a great deal of solar energy toward the space station. This reflected energy warms the condenser and hampers it in its task of cooling the vapor from the turbines.

Von Braun has equipped his satellite station with one of these solar engines, but he has not too much confidence in it, and he hopes that when the time comes to build a satellite, something better will turn up. One of his hopes is that the power for the station may be drawn from an ingot of radioactive metal—polonium for instance—which keeps its temperature far above that of its surroundings. Such a convenient power package will heat a working fluid so strongly that even a small condenser will cool it sufficiently to maintain the power cycle. Even better would be a stock of radioactive material that gives a direct flow of electrical energy. No such treasure is in sight at present.

Many readers must have wondered by this time whether a satellite placed in its orbit with such enormous effort has any practical use. To this question each space enthusiast has his own private answer.

Some think that the triumph of leaving the earth, and later of landing on Mars or Venus, should be sufficient in itself to enlist the co-operation of the entire human race. They claim that the conquest of space will be much cheaper in money and effort than even a minor war, which brings satisfaction to few and misery to many.

Another group believes that the space project will pay off in engineering techniques developed while making the effort. They point to the medieval alchemists who never succeeded in transmuting base metals into gold, but whose frantic pursuit of this chimera laid the foundations of the science of chemistry. The crusades were impractical too, and they did not succeed, but the knowledge that the survivors brought back from Moslem countries ended Europe's age of darkness.

Another group of enthusiasts led by Arthur C. Clarke, chairman of the British Interplanetary Society, believes that man may thrive better in space, living there permanently, than he does at the bottom of the atmosphere. Some of these possible benefits will be considered in a later chapter. A more immediate benefit has been offered to the United States by von Braun, who almost made his V-2s pay off in victory for Hitler.

Von Braun appears to be a practical man if he is not looked at too closely. He speaks incisively with the faintest German accent, and he can and has impressed both German and American military experts. He can also inspire an audience of civilian engineers, or of kids, or of theoretical scientists, or of mush-minded faddists.

The satellite station, says von Braun, looking the military leaders of his host nation straight in the eye, will pay off as nothing has done since the time of the Roman legions. If placed in its orbit by the United States, it will give the United States permanent military control of the entire earth. No nation will challenge the power that looks down upon it from an artificial moon. No nation will attempt to challenge it; the earth will enjoy a *pax Americana* and can beat its radars into television sets.

The satellite station, explains von Braun, will provide the two essentials of successful war: observation and bombardment. It will swing around the earth once every two hours, and as the earth slowly turns beneath it on its own axis, every part of its surface will come into view. At the satellite's distance of more than a thousand miles, few human activities can be watched with the naked eye, but the eyes of the men in the satellite will be by no means naked.

Telescopes work much better in space than they do in the atmosphere, since the sharpness of their definition is not reduced by small disturbances in nearby air. Von Braun maintains that a hundred-inch telescope parked in steady space beside the satellite station can observe or photograph objects on the surface of the earth that are only sixteen inches in diameter.

Every movement of men or machines in Soviet Russia, for instance, would be visible from the satellite. Space-borne observers could even keep track of the changing of the Kremlin guard. Larger objects, such as Russian airfields, factories, troop movements or strategic railroads would show up plain as day. No Iron Curtain would be proof against prying eyes in space.

To observe the enemy's moves is the first step of war; the second step is to smack him down when he makes a hostile move. Von Braun believes that this can be done efficiently from the satellite station. He proposes to do it with small, atom-armed guided missiles sent down to earth along the path of his returning shuttle rockets.

They will have rocket motors just powerful enough to put them into descending ellipses. When they reach the atmosphere, they can be steered by radio signals acting on their controls. Their courses will carry them along close under the satellite traveling on its orbit, so they will be under observation by telescope or radar during their entire descent. This is highly desirable, von Braun points out, in the guided-missile business. The target (say a Russian plutonium installation) will also be in view from the satellite. So the missile's course can be corrected continuously, making a direct hit almost inevitable. The atomic bomb in the missile's nose will take care of terminal action.

Von Braun maintains that a satellite, or perhaps a series of them strung like beads on the orbit, will assure global control. A school of fierce little missiles will follow each satellite, and great shining mirrors will search the earth below, reporting any hostile activity to appropriate control centers in the United States. Orders from below will tell the space men which targets to destroy. Von Braun believes that few such orders will be necessary.

Counteraction by the Russians, says von Braun, will have no hope of success. The vast preparations necessary for a rocket attack on one of the space stations would surely be detected from the orbit. The unfinished installations would be denounced as threats to global peace and destroyed from above by a shower of atomic missiles. Even if rockets did manage to struggle up from below, von Braun believes that they could be repelled with ease by the superior equipment of the garrison entrenched in space.

10

CHORUS OF MISGIVING

Von Braun has pushed his satellite proposal in lectures, books and gaudily illustrated magazine articles. He talks eloquently and writes well. He has won an enormous following, not only among the technically naive, but among that even more credulous type, the semi-technical enthusiasts who have recently graduated from playing with hot-rod jalopies. All over the United States and in many other parts of the world are groups of enthusiasts who dream of hot-rodding off the tedious earth. Von Braun is their hero because he tells them that it can be done in only ten years or so.

In more informed circles, von Braun is no hero. Almost all the men who work with rockets and guided missiles are space-travel enthusiasts in their own way. They read science fiction with critical enjoyment. They think that space flight will come and hope that it will come soon. They are men of deep technological faith who believe that anything can be done with sufficient time and effort.

But von Braun's proposal gives them cold chills. They spend their lives with detonating fuels, melting metals and psychotic artificial brains. They have seen many beautiful rockets explode into whizzing fragments or flop to inglorious ends a few hundred yards from their launching sites. They know that each forward step is difficult and dangerous, and they believe that von Braun proposes to take one thousand steps as if they were one. They say that von Braun's great shuttle rockets—to say nothing of his space station—would surely fail, probably in a gigantic fiasco that would sour the world on space flight for the next hundred years.

Neither von Braun nor his critics can debate frankly in public. Von Braun now works for Army Ordnance as a civilian expert at its guided-missile development center at Redstone Arsenal, Huntsville, Alabama. His job is with practical military missiles, not with space ships, but nearly all the facts and developments that have to do with space flight are also facts about missiles and are therefore rigidly secret. He cannot tell what he knows without risking drastic punishment as well as breaking his oath. His opponents have the same difficulty. When they debate with him, they must limit themselves to rather general opinions. Most of them prefer not to debate at all; they are too much afraid of giving away vital military secrets.

One expert who has debated publicly but carefully with von Braun is Dr. Milton Rosen of the Naval Research Laboratory, Washington, D.C. He can talk with more freedom than most of the missile men because he is head of the Navy's Viking Project, and the Viking is a high-altitude research rocket, not a military missile. Many things about it are secret because any rocket information is of military value, but Dr. Rosen feels that his work does not compel him to be quite as tongue-tied as most of the other experts.

Dr. Rosen is not an emotional man, but his face turns almost white with horror as he talks about difficulties that von Braun passes over as gaily as if they did not exist. It would take too long, he says, to enumerate all of them. Every ambitious rocket contains a long series of intricate components, and every single part, down to valves and gaskets and relays, must work with absolute perfection or the whole rocket will fail.

Even minor changes of design invite total disaster. Many a new rocket, including some of Rosen's, has failed because some insignificant part has not been sufficiently tested. Von Braun should know this, says Rosen. The history of his V-2 development featured a long series of hair-raising disasters, and the V-2 was a conservative vehicle when compared with the 7,000-ton monsters that von Braun proposes to send up to the orbit.

Rosen explains that the necessity of testing and retesting every design and every part makes rocket progress necessarily slow. This has been the history of all the American guided missiles that have now reached a point of perfection where they can be used in war. The early models balked or exploded, failed to find their targets or failed to rise at all. The files of White Sands and the Pentagon bulge with their records of failure. Many promising missiles that cost thousands of man-years of skillful work have been abandoned permanently. Most of the missiles that the public has heard about are these long-abandoned models whose disclosure is no longer considered a threat to military secrecy.

Dr. Rosen does not quarrel with the theorists who maintain that flight into space is possible. He admits that chemical fuels—even those in use already—can be burned in a large multi-stage rocket to place a small payload in a satellite orbit. The cost will be tremendous. For each ton of payload carried up to the orbit, nearly 170 tons of expensive fuel will have to be burned. The present cost of hydrazine, one of von Braun's favorite fuels, is about $5,000 per ton.

To maintain the satellite in its orbit and supply its crew with food, water and oxygen to breathe will require a shuttle of gigantic rockets, each taking off from its island base with a flood of flame like a volcanic eruption. Von Braun insists that the shuttle rockets, or at least their manned third stages, can be used many times. Dr. Rosen disagrees emphatically. He thinks that each shuttle rocket can be used only once and that its crew will be expendable too. The cost of building fleets of shuttle rockets and of training crews to be sacrificed in them will raise the carrying charge of each ton of payload to a fantastic figure.

Perhaps the cost could be borne by the United States. A more serious objection is that von Braun's proposal would certainly fail—no matter how much money is lavished upon it. It is too great a jump, says Rosen, into the technological future. A vital project can be speeded up by the "crash" procedure of trying many things at once with the knowledge that many will fail, but even this costly policy has its limit. Some problems must be solved in series, first one, then another. Until the first problem is solved, it is utterly useless to start work on those that depend upon it.

"And what's the hurry, anyway?" asks Dr. Rosen. He looks with a cold naval eye on von Braun's contention that the satellite station will allow the United States to dominate the earth. This is just not so, he says.

Supplying the station with instruments to keep watch on Soviet Russia would be enormously difficult, and many parts of the instrument-development program could not be started until the satellite is actually established in space. The capabilities of the crews under the satellite's living conditions would have to be learned by practical experience. As for the guided missiles that the satellite will launch, Rosen believes that they would be lucky to hit the right country.

The satellite project, in Rosen's opinion, would have a negative military value equivalent to a major defeat in the cold war. The United States is suffering at present from an agonizing scarcity of qualified engineers and scientists. Every corporation and government agency that deals with technical matters is beating the bushes for men who know the difference between a slide rule and an oscilloscope. They have long since abandoned the normal recruitment methods; they buy full-page ads in magazines and make appeals over the radio. They send recruiting parties to every university and technical school. Each graduating student has scores of offers to consider. Each man who has a job already knows that a job as good or better waits for him over the fence of his nearest corporate neighbor.

This shortage of qualified men has slowed down or frustrated nearly every kind of project. The most spectacular pinch is in electronics, but all other specialties are almost as starved for men. Computing machines often stand idle because there are not enough mathematicians to feed problems into them. Even specialists who have no direct connection with military developments are scarce too. Not long ago the great Monsanto Chemical Company needed a troop of botanists. It did not find them.

Dr. Rosen believes that if von Braun's proposal were put into motion with the strength of the government behind it, it would sop up almost the entire supply of American technical men—from astronomers to zoologists. Thousands of other projects would have to stop. Hardest hit would be the guided-missile program which military planners consider vital to American security. Von Braun's rockets might not struggle into space for many decades. In the meantime the nation's military technology would fall far behind the Russians'. It would be a gigantic gamble, like betting the nation's survival on a single number of a roulette wheel.

When practical guided-missile men like Rosen and his colleagues hear that von Braun's proposal is being seriously considered in high military circles, they scream for salvation from it. But the rumors keep filtering down along the tortuous channels that zigzag out from the Pentagon. Von Braun's satellite proposal is not the only one. An agency working for the Air Force has outlined a similar project; so have at least two of the great airplane companies.

The merits of all of them, of course, are discussed in the thickest secrecy, so the missile men on the working level are never entirely sure what the decision has been. Some of the more cynical ones suspect that space flight has become involved in the fierce interservice battles that are fought inside the Pentagon. If the Army, the Navy or the Air Force could sell a satellite program to the President and Congress, it would leave the competing services hopelessly behind. The same glittering prize excites the airplane manufacturers. They would love to build rockets as big as cruisers and shoot them into space, never to return, at many million dollars each shot. So when the practical missile men hear about vice admirals and three-star Air Force generals participating in public discussions of von Braun's satellite proposal, they scent Pentagon politics and pray for delivery from it. They believe that a race into space by two or more of the services would be a national disaster.

At White Sands Proving Ground, where rockets are tangible things, von Braun's theories are received with a curious mixture of fascination and alarm. The men of White Sands do not deride the general idea of space flight. They seem to feel toward it an almost religious reverence. But when they examine the details of von Braun's project, they see a bristling array of menacing obstacles, and each man sees the worst difficulties in the specialty that he knows best.

The propulsion experts, for instance, point out that large rocket motors are still extremely unstable. The combustion process that goes on inside them is understood only empirically, so each new motor is packed with unpleasant surprises. If the dimensions of a motor are increased by even a small factor, all sorts of novel effects show up, most of them undesirable. Even well-known motors must be babied along to keep them from exploding, melting or shaking themselves to pieces.

When two or more motors are used in the same rocket, the chances of disaster are increased sharply. Von Braun's great first-stage rocket will contain 51 motors, each of them exerting a thrust of 275 tons. Motors as big as this may have been tested recently, but to judge from the expressions on the faces of the rocket men (who cannot give details) the tests cannot have been entirely satisfactory.

To use 51 of these unpredictable monsters and count on all of them performing with complete perfection appears to the propulsion experts as something close to lunacy. The failure of a single motor would make the whole flight fail. The explosion of one of them would make the whole rocket crash in a vast disaster that would cover square miles of country with a sea of flame.

The propulsion experts admit that rockets as big as von Braun's can be built eventually, but they think that to make them fly successfully will take much more than ten years of trial and unavoidable error. The mathematics of combustion will have to be understood much better than at present, and this requires genius as well as sweat and time. New heat-resisting materials must be developed to stand the long strain of the climb into space. New fuels will have to be studied and manufactured in quantity, and they are all so dangerous that time-consuming catastrophes are almost inevitable.

If the great new motors are to be used in clusters, they must be tested in clusters. A test stand must be constructed that can handle their combined thrust of 14,000 tons. To design and build this enormous and delicate structure and to instrument it properly will be an effort of years in itself. Then will follow many years of failure strung out by long periods of baffled frustration. Then, when the first rocket flies, any one of a thousand small failings may bring it back to earth at 10,000 miles per hour.

The experts concerned with control equipment are dubious too. The rocket's ascent cannot be a simple shot into space. It must follow exactly a carefully planned course, and if it deviates from it even by a little, it will fail to attain the necessary speed and altitude.

To accomplish this feat by means of automatic instruments is exceedingly difficult. Three-stage rockets are not merely three times as hard to control as single-stage rockets. Each stage adds multiplying difficulties and sources of error. A slight deviation at the beginning of the flight is magnified many times before the flight is over.

Until the rocket has reached the comparative security of the final orbit, the crew can do nothing to meet unforeseen emergencies. There will be many of these, and the automatic controls will have to deal with them somehow. Such controls can be developed; the men of technological faith have no doubt about this. But it will take a great deal of time, thought, and trial and error, and no one can be sure how the new devices will work until several rockets have actually flown to the orbit.

Some of the instruments and equipment needed on the space rocket can be developed on earth. One example of this is the positioning device that uses flywheels or gyroscopes to turn the space-borne rocket in a desired direction. Other devices can be tested only in true flight. No wind tunnel on the surface can match the conditions of tremendous speed, high temperature and almost absolute vacuum that the rocket will meet on the fringes of space. It is possible to estimate from theory how its wings and control surfaces will react to these extreme trials, but aerodynamic experts do not trust such guesses.

The most pessimistic group of missile men are those

who specialize on getting equipment down undamaged from the top of the atmosphere. All high-altitude rockets flown at White Sands have come to violent ends. The highest-flying rocket so far, the two-stage WAC Corporal that rose from the nose of a soaring V-2 and reached the altitude of 250 miles, came back to earth with parts of its fins melted into metal rain. Sometimes rockets are deliberately blown into two parts during their descent. This destroys their streamlining and makes the parts fall more slowly, thus preserving some of the instrument records that they contain. They still hit the earth hard enough, however, to smash anything that is not protected in strong steel cells. No parachute has proved effective so far when used in rockets descending from above fifty miles. A parachute melts, even though made of steel ribbons or strands.

The recovery experts all feel the deepest sympathy for the heroic crews of von Braun's returning rockets. They do not deny that a winged rocket can, theoretically, skim through the near vacuum of the outer atmosphere and keep itself at a temperature that will not melt its wings. But the stunt will be frightfully difficult, and the slightest accident, malfunctioning, error or miscalculation will result in instant disaster. All exterior parts of the ship will be red hot, and every engineer knows how many unpredictable failures this condition produces.

Von Braun seems to assume that the outer fringe of the atmosphere is uniform and stable all the way round the earth. This is not true. Not much is known about the outermost layers, but rocket flights have already proved that they are anything but stable. There are tides in the atmosphere, as in the ocean, and they bulge its limits outward in an unknown manner and to an unknown distance.

Some layers of the upper atmosphere are strongly heated by sunlight, and this is known to stir them to violent turbulence, like the thunderstorms that form near the surface of the earth at the end of a hot day. Dr. Rosen's Viking rockets have brought back evidence that high, thin winds blow vertically in the upper atmosphere at something like 100 miles per hour. The air at that altitude is also in horizontal movement, probably just as violent.

To judge by analogy with the weather at lower altitudes, these movements of the outer air probably change with the seasons and with fluctuations of solar radiation. They must follow day and night, but no one knows just how. They may even be affected by such apparent trifles as the trails of meteors, which heat and rarefy the air they pass through.

So the pilot of von Braun's winged rocket cannot count on still air to fly in. It will be full of uncharted bumps, and an encounter with one of them may buckle his softened wings. A powerful wind blowing downward may drop him suddenly into denser air. Then his ship will turn in an instant into a streak of fire.

11

HOSTILE ENVIRONMENT

What about human bodies and brains? How well will they function under the strange and violent conditions in space, and in space ships climbing up toward it? The handful of men who study this question seriously are not optimistic. They are willing to admit for the sake of argument that rockets can reach space, but they are not happy about the fate of their human crews.

Any consideration of this problem brings up a striking conception that lies behind all thought on man's adaptation to space. The transition to life outside the atmosphere will be so abrupt and fundamental that it can be compared to nothing less than the colonization of the land by creatures from the sea.

Space flight is not comparable to any other kind of locomotion. It involves penetration into a hostile medium that is wholly different from the sheltered bottom of the atmosphere. The best way to appreciate the difficulty of this step is to look at the closest precedent: the adaptation of man's fish ancestors to life on the hostile land.

Life originated in the sea and developed in it slowly for hundreds of millions of years, while the land surfaces of the ancient earth remained utterly lifeless. The primitive, soft-bodied sea creatures, many of them hardly more dense than the water itself, were utterly unable to colonize it. The gleaming surface above their heads was a deadly, impassable boundary. They had developed in water, and without water all around them they could not live.

But life tries everything over and over until something works. There were tides in that ancient life-packed ocean, and since the moon was closer then and the earth revolved more rapidly, the tides were more violent than they are today. The plants and animals of the sea were forever being stranded on lifeless, clamless mud flats.

Nearly all of them died as soon as the water left them and the sun struck down on their soft, wet bodies. But as evolution created more forms, some of them proved tough enough to live a few hours on the land. These survived until the tide came back to rescue them. In the case of organisms that lived in bays and tidal pools where stranding was common, the ability to survive a short exposure to sunlight was a powerful competitive advantage. The toughest individuals left more descendants, and these were further selected for toughness by stranding in turn. So life marched little by little up the tidal flats, up the rivers, over the soggy deltas, over the coastal areas where rain was frequent and water was never wholly absent.

The first to colonize the land were undoubtedly plants, for animals are dependent on plants and cannot live without them. But as soon as the plants were established on dry land, animals followed to devour them. We can only guess vaguely what these pioneers looked like, but we can list their difficulties and how they overcame them.

All this may seem to have little to do with man's problems as he aspires toward space, but there is a close analogy. As the ancient sea creatures moved out on the land, they fought their way with frightful losses into a deadly new medium—the air. In the process of learning to live on the land, they were forced to acquire higher abilities than were needed in the sea. This was true of both plants and animals. One of nature's basic laws is that obstacles overcome give strength to overcome more obstacles.

The venturesome sea creatures were not contemplative. Their brains were too ill organized to give them even the illusion of consciousness. But if they had been able to think philosophically about their conquest of the land, they would have been both appalled and inspired, as modern men are inspired when they think about the conquest of space.

Let us imagine for a moment that some sluglike sea creature, creeping above the surface of the sea, has a brain that can enumerate the hostile conditions that he will meet in the air. He will miss the friendly water in dozens of ways. In the sea it brings him oxygen and other chemicals. The air is rich in oxygen—so rich that it may be poisonous—but it contains nothing else that his body needs. Moreover, it has a fearful effect: it dries up the water in his body. So an animal that aspires to life on the land must have a tough integument to protect its tissues from drying. Men in space will need similar protection against the vacuum around them.

As soon as our soft, wet pioneer creeps above the water's surface, he will be assailed by a blast of solar radiation. The sea is sunlit too, but its water acts as a filter, screening out many of the frequencies in the spectrum of sunlight. Above the surface there is less protection. A much wider spectrum beats down from the sun, and parts of it are deadly to tender cells from the sea. So the pioneers that aspire to life on land must also learn how to protect themselves from hostile radiation.

Temperature changes are deadly too. The sea is a placid place in respect to temperature. Its surface warms slowly in summer and cools slowly in winter. A few fathoms down it warms and cools hardly at all. Sea animals are so badly spoiled by this evenness that a slight change of temperature will kill them suddenly. To them the temperature changes of the air above seem horribly violent. The air grows deadly cold when the sun sets, and as deadly hot when the sun rises. A change of wind or the drift of a cloud produces temperature changes that seem cruelly sudden to a creature accustomed to the sea. If it aspires to live in the air, it must learn to protect its tender tissues from quick fluctuations of temperature. Man in space will have the same problem.

The most mysterious, baffling force that faced the pioneers was certainly gravitation. In the sea gravitation is mild and easily allowed for. The bodies of most sea animals are made chiefly of water, and they match its specific gravity almost exactly. Those forms that desire to float near the sea's surface contain small globules of oil to make them light enough to do so. Those that want to stay on the bottom may ballast themselves with heavy material such as calcium carbonate shell. The freely swimming forms need make only feeble movements to keep themselves at any desired level. They do not feel the weight of their bodies, since the water that their bodies displace weighs almost the same. This friendly condition permits soft animals like jellyfish, which may be as large as umbrellas, to maneuver skillfully in the water with only flypower muscles.

Above the surface of the sea, gravitation is shockingly powerful. It strikes down with a fearful force, crushing soft bodies into helpless pancakes. It presses them against sand or mud, creating so much friction that their small powers of locomotion cannot tear them free.

On every modern beach the ebbing tide leaves thousands of helpless victims struggling with gravitation. Jellyfish give up at once and dry to thin films as the air steals their moisture. Squids and fish struggle a little longer. Whales that are grounded on sand bars live for hours. They can breathe the air, since their ancestors once lived on land, but relentless gravitation pulling from the center of the earth crushes their great flabby bodies. They die of internal distortion.

Sea creatures that wish to live on the land must have special means to cope with gravitation. They need strong, solid skeletons to support their soft tissues. They need powerful muscles if they want to move at all. If they want to move rapidly in the free gravitational field, they need legs of some sort to hold their bodies clear of the surface of the earth. They need good nervous systems to co-ordinate the motions of their legs.

Many waves of life have crept out of the sea during the last half-billion years. Some of the smallest forms made only minor adjustments, keeping to the films of water between soil particles. Slightly more ambitious types, such as the shelly mollusks, dragged solid capsules with them. They did not attempt to move rapidly, and when the air became too dry or the sun beat down too fiercely, they crawled into some sheltered spot and sealed themselves tightly into their protective shells.

The really successful land pioneers made more radical changes. The insects surrounded their tissues with tough outer skeletons to support them and protect them from drying and radiation. They developed strong muscles and excellent nervous systems. They did not permit the hostile air to come in uncontrolled contact with their internal moisture. Insects breathe through small, branching tubes that carry oxygen where it is needed.

In a purely physical sense, they have made the most perfect adjustment to life in the air, but their unyielding external skeleton and the limited capacity of their breathing system does not permit them to function effectively in sizes larger than a mouse.

The most successful wave of life that ventured out of the sea carried the sea with it. The primitive vertebrate fish that first pioneered the land had well-developed hearts and circulation systems. Their veins and arteries were filled essentially with sea water that carried oxygen and nutrients to the cells of their bodies and carried away waste products such as carbon dioxide. Instead of junking this system when they crawled out on the land, the adventurous fish took it with them, intact and almost unchanged. The blood of their distant descendants, including men, is Paleozoic sea water. It is not as salty as modern sea water; it has almost the exact composition that geologists assign to the sea when the ancestral fish first crawled out of it.

The long history of life's development and its painful emergence from the sheltering sea gives a foretaste of the adjustments that man must make if his sea-born, air-accustomed body is to rise above still another boundary and stay alive in space. All the enemies that struck at the sea creatures when they ventured into the air will strike with redoubled vindictiveness at the human pioneers who climb above the atmosphere.

Above the air that now shelters man as the sea once sheltered his ancestors are raw astronomical forces. The emptiness of space is hostile in itself, but space is not mere emptiness. It clashes and roars with meteors, cosmic rays, hot-breathed radiation and strange gravitational fields.

At Randolph Field, San Antonio, Texas, works a small group of men whose duty is to look into space and weigh its perils. Their official name is the Division of Space Medicine of the Air Force School of Aviation Medicine. There are only a few of these men and some of them are Germans who began their imaginative work in the *Luftwaffe* under Hitler. To talk with them is a strange and thrilling experience. As these Air Force officers and professors from Heidelberg look up at the sky above the plains of Texas, they are like the Paleozoic fish, talking (if the fish could have talked) about the dangers that would assail them when they decided to crawl above the surface of their pool.

Using the scientific method of dissecting a many-sided problem into its separate parts, the space doctors discuss and study the dangers of space individually, but they keep in mind an overwhelming fact: that when man climbs fully clear of his pool, all his enemies will hit him simultaneously. The crews of space ships will have to be protected against the entire battery of death-dealing effects.

One enemy—airlessness—has struck already at the pilots who fly modern jet planes. At about 13,000 feet, the thinning of the air begins to affect them seriously, making them breathe hard and making their brains function less effectively. Simple masks that give them oxygen to breathe allow them to fly without discomfort to 20,000 feet. Above this level even pure oxygen does not suffice. The cabins must be made airtight and pumped full of air at something like surface pressure.

This has been done in most high-flying airplanes. In effect, the pilots take with them the atmosphere that they were accustomed to on the surface of the earth. They are analogous to the ancient fish that took with them out of the sea the water in which they had evolved.

The pilots thin-walled capsules of pressurized air, moving above the speed of sound in the partial vacuum of the stratosphere, are fragile and precarious things. They may lose their pressure suddenly through mechanical failure or enemy action, and one of the duties of the space doctors is to figure out what will happen and how fast it will happen when a cozy capsule loses its pressure. By experimenting with animals, and sometimes with human volunteers in vacuum chambers, they have drawn up a rather horrible timetable of these unpleasant effects.

If the cabin loses its pressure at 45,000 feet, for instance, the pilot will have what the space doctors call "useful consciousness" for about 30 seconds. During this brief period he must turn his plane downward in hope of reaching richer air before the blackout that sweeps over him turns into permanent death.

At 55,000 feet the period of useful consciousness diminishes to 15 seconds. The thin air outside the broken canopy is of no use to the pilot. Its pressure is too low. Even if he breathes pure oxygen as hard as he can, he cannot clear away the carbon dioxide accumulating in his lungs. In 15 seconds he blacks out, his sensitive brain cells starved for oxygen. In a few more seconds he is dead.

At 63,000 feet, death comes even quicker and in a horrifying way. The outside pressure is so low that water boils at the temperature of the human blood. So the pilot's blood turns in an instant into a thick red froth, and his flesh swells up like biscuits baking in an oven. Death is almost instantaneous.

The space doctors are glumly amused when they see the comely boys and girls of the comic strips climbing around outside their space ships or cheerfully skirmishing with villains on airless asteroids. They are generally dressed for Miami Beach with only a bubble of plastic over their attractive faces. Sometimes as a grudging concession to the facts of space, they wear loose coveralls that do not hamper their movements.

The comic-strip artists and many of the space-fiction writers seem to believe that what people need to keep them alive in space is protection from something that comes from outside. What they need most is protection from the water in their own tissues. It must be kept from expanding into vapor and tearing them apart, and to do this is difficult.

Two approaches have been tried, neither of them very successfully. The first, identified with the Navy, was to encase a man entirely in a heavy rubber suit with a helmet coming down over his chest, and accordion-jointed limbs. This full pressure suit has been publicized as a true space suit that might be worn on the moon.

It is no such thing. Its airtight construction makes it insufferably and dangerously uncomfortable. When it is inflated, it blows up like an anthropomorphic balloon and is difficult to walk in or to work in effectively. It is possible that the full pressure suit can be improved, but few informed people have much hope for it.

The second approach is a suit that can be made so tight that it keeps the water in the wearer's tissues from turning to vapor when the outside pressure fails. After an enormous amount of effort, the Air Force has developed a garment of this sort that it calls a partial pressure suit. It is a tight-fitting union suit of strong greenish cloth. A rigid helmet fits over the wearer's head, and inside the suit and along the limbs are flat rubber bladders with flexible tubes connecting them to a cylinder of high-pressure oxygen.

When the airplane's cockpit loses its pressure, an automatic valve snaps open, allowing oxygen to flow into the helmet and the rubber bladders. Their expansion tightens the suit, supplying a substitute pressure around the wearer's body so that his warm blood does not flash at once into deadly froth. Dressed in this way, he can stay alive in a vacuum for about ten minutes. He can move with enough freedom to work the controls of his damaged airplane and try to turn it downward to lifesaving air. But he is not comfortable. His hands, which are not fully pressurized, swell up quickly with blue venous blood. He breathes with difficulty. His neck just below his helmet is a ring of pain. The space doctors have not figured how to pressurize his neck without causing strangulation.

A pilot dressed in this way may be able to save his life when his canopy is punctured, but he is not prepared for carefree frisking in a vacuum. The loveliest space girl perched on an asteroid would not get a moment s attention from a tortured human struggling just ahead of death in a partial pressure suit.

When the space doctors assay the problem of how to make men live at ease in a vacuum, they are not optimistic. The human body demands an outside pressure of at least ten pounds per square inch, and the suit must provide it. So the walls must be strong, and the many joints that are necessary for mobility must be both flexible and leakproof because a loss of pressure means instant death. The moisture and carbon dioxide given off by the body must be disposed of somehow, and the temperature inside the suit must be kept within narrow limits. To provide these services for only a few hours will require more apparatus than a single man can handle.

So the space doctors have almost given up. Dr. Fritz Haber of the Air Force Division of Space Medicine believes that if humans want to work in the vacuum outside their space ships, they must do it in solid-walled cylinders, each provided with elaborate air-conditioning apparatus. If they want to walk on the surface of the moon, they will have to do so by means of tracks or leg-like appendages operated from inside. If they want to build a lunar city, they will have to do the work with metal arms and hands like the remotely controlled manipulators used by atomic scientists to handle radioactive material from behind thick concrete shields.

The peril of airlessness, which is equivalent to the waterlessness that troubled man's aquatic ancestors, has already been encountered. Man's highest-flying planes such as the Bell X-1 and the Douglas Skyrocket have already flown to altitudes where the air is so thin that it might as well be a vacuum so far as human bodies are concerned. The other perils of space have not yet been met at full force, but it is the duty of the space doctors to anticipate and outwit them. They gather each bit of information brought down from space by rockets and try to calculate how human bodies will react when they pass entirely out of the atmosphere.

One unexpected problem is violent temperature changes, strikingly analogous to the temperature problems that the ancient fish had to solve as they crawled out of the sea and met the sun face-to-face for the first time. Heat caused by air friction has long been familiar to airplane designers. High-speed airplanes get so hot from friction that they must be cooled by elaborate air-conditioning systems. Much progress has been made toward cracking this so-called "heat barrier," but the problem of heat in space itself is entirely different. No matter how fast a rocket or space ship moves, it normally meets no air to cause friction. Heat comes from a different source—the glaring, unscreened sunlight.

Space is often spoken of as cold—"the terrible cold of

outer space"—but the truth is that space can have no temperature at all. Temperature is due to the movement of molecules, and there are too few molecules in space to make it either hot or cold.

The temperature of material objects floating in space is determined by the balance between the heat that they receive by radiation and the heat that they radiate away. A comet rounding the end of its orbit ten billion miles from the sun is certainly very cold. It receives little sunlight, and the heat that it may have contained has long since been dissipated. But when the comet turns and plunges toward the sun, it begins to get more heat and its temperature rises. The nearer it comes, the hotter it gets, and if it whips close enough to the sun's flaming surface, it gets so hot that much of its substance is vaporized.

Man's space vehicles will do well to keep away from the sun, but even at the earth's distance of 92 million miles, sunlight is strong enough to make them uninhabitable if their surfaces are such that they absorb its energy and fail to radiate it quickly. The surface of the moon, which is an airless space ship, reaches 270° F. when full sunlight is falling on it.

Each material of which space vehicles might be made behaves in a characteristic way when exposed to sunlight in space. The most familiar material, polished aluminum, behaves very badly. It absorbs a large part of the solar energy and radiates little of it. Therefore its temperature may rise as high as 850° F. At the other extreme are white pigments that reflect most of the solar radiation, absorbing very little of it. At the same time, they radiate heat efficiently. So their temperature, even when exposed to sunlight, often gets as low as −40° F.

It is possible to cover a space ship with a material that will absorb and radiate in such a way that the interior temperature remains at a comfortable level. But the balance is delicate and easily upset. A rocket-shaped space vehicle, for instance, might be comfortable when one of its long sides is exposed to sunlight falling on it at a right angle. But if it turns 90 degrees to point toward the sun, the amount of sunlight hitting it will be sharply reduced, while the amount of heat radiating into space will remain the same. Then the inside temperature will drop suddenly far below zero. The drop will be even sharper if the vehicle passes into the shadow of the earth.

Keeping the interior temperature tolerable is one of those problems which space enthusiasts believe can be licked by mere engineering skill, but it will require a great deal of elaborate and automatic apparatus, such as shutters to cover or expose heat-absorbing areas. Special coatings will have to be developed, and they must be dependable. If a white coating should peel off for any reason, exposing polished metal to sunlight, the space ship's crew might be baked like potatoes in a few minutes.

Lack of protection against radiant heat is one of the many flaws in those familiar magazine illustrations of men in space suits propelled to and from their work by personal rockets bearing against their navels. If made of black rubber, for instance, their suits would be hot enough on the sunny side to burn the skin, and far below zero on the shady side. If painted white, they would be deadly cold on both sides.

This temperature balance would change with each movement of the wearer. If he should enter the shadow of his ship, his temperature would drop close to absolute zero. If he should get radiation both from the sun and from the sunlit earth below, his suit would get hot enough on both sides to destroy any flexible material and cook its human contents.

Insulation to protect the man from the heat or cold of his suit would have to be inches thick, and it would have to cover his face as well as the rest of his body. This temperature difficulty is an additional reason why light and handy space suits are not admired by the space doctors.

Heat is not the only enemy that comes from the sun. The fierce solar radiation that streams through space contains ultraviolet rays that never reach the earth's surface. They are screened out by the atmosphere, just as some of their companion wave lengths were screened out by the sea water and never reached its inhabitants. They are deadly to living cells that have never had to deal with them.

So when man rises above the atmosphere, he will have to screen his tissues from the hostile ultraviolet, just as the sea creatures had to screen themselves from the unfamiliar parts of the spectrum. This is not too hard; ultraviolet is stopped by almost any substance.

But it does not stop without a struggle. It quickly destroys many binders that are used in paints, as well as most of the flexible plastic or textile materials that man counts on so heavily. These cannot be used above the atmosphere because they disintegrate when they are exposed to ultraviolet. Rubber space suits would certainly go to pieces quickly.

Even familiar, visible light kicks up trouble in space. On the sheltered surface of the earth, much of the light from the sun has been scattered by the air that it has passed through. This is why the sky is blue, for blue light is scattered more than the other colors.

In bright sunlight, only about three-fourths of the light that hits a spot on the earth's surface comes to it straight from the sun. The final one-fourth comes by scattering from the blue sky. This diffuse light strikes into shadows and makes objects in them visible, even when no sunlight reaches them directly.

Sunlight in space, which is much more powerful than on the earth, is not scattered at all. The sky looks black, with swarms of untwinkling stars shining brightly in it. Shadows cast by the sun are as black as puddles of ink. The only light that reaches them is starlight and it is too feeble to register on the human retina.

This glaring contrast will be hard on human eyes, which are not designed to adjust quickly from blackness to full sunlight. The interiors of space ships can be illuminated artificially or by means of small windows with frosted glass to supply diffuse light, but when a space traveler looks out on the universe around him, he must guard his sensitive eyes against too great changes of lighting. He must never glance at the sun for an instant. His pupils, adjusted to the blackness of the general sky, will be wide open. Even a flick of full sun will dazzle into them dangerously. He must be almost as careful when looking at large sunlit bodies such as the earth or the moon. They will dazzle his dark-adjusted eyes almost as violently as the sun itself.

Space travelers who try to operate outside their ships will see alternate patches of painful glare and black shadow. This will inconvenience them even if they have been provided with efficient space suits. When the object with which they are working happens to be in full sunlight, their eyes will contract to pinpoints to shut out its glare. Then everything that is in shadow will be as invisible as if it were nonexistent. Even the space traveler's hands will disappear from his sight when they move into a shadow.

Or if he is working on an object in shadow, his eyes will have to be sensitive enough to see by the faint light reflected upon it by sunlit objects nearby. His pupils will open full, and the rods and cones of his retina will strain toward their full sensitivity as if he were walking on a moonless night under a star-filled sky. Then, if he inadvertently glances at a sunlit object a few feet away from his hands, his eyes will be dazzled and blinded by the stab of its light. Space doctors are fearful that human eyes, which evolved under the gentle conditions beneath the atmosphere, will not be able to stand many such light-shocks.

The most mysterious terror of space is the cosmic rays. They are atomic particles—most of them protons but some of them as heavy as atoms of iron—that come from the depths of space, no one knows where. They have nothing to do with the sun. Just as many hit the earth on the side away from the sun as on the side toward it. They have not been traced to any star or group of stars. They stream toward the earth from emptiness at a constant rate and with speed and energy up to hundreds of billions of electron-volts.

When these violent particles reach the fringe of the atmosphere, they hit air molecules and smash them and themselves into showers of fragments—electrons, protons, mesons, etc.—which pepper the earth in a spreading cone like pellets from a shotgun. Some of the secondary particles hit other air atoms and start smaller patterns of fragments. Most of these never reach the earth's surface; they are absorbed by the air. Only a few run the gantlet, but some of them carry so much energy that they penetrate hundreds of feet into the solid earth. No shield, however massive, gives appreciable protection against cosmic rays.

Life grew up with the cosmic rays ever since it began. It may indeed have been started by their action on chemical substances dissolved in the primitive sea. The genetic mutations that are an essential factor in the process of evolution are due in part to cosmic rays that have struck and damaged the genes in the nuclei of reproductive cells. An organism that grows out of these damaged genes may have a slightly different form, and if this form gives it an advantage in the competitive struggle for life, the evolution of that particular species moves a small step forward.

But the flux of cosmic rays at the surface of the earth is like a gentle pattering shower compared to the fierce bombardment that strikes the top of the atmosphere. With each increase in altitude, the rays become more powerful. At 45,000 feet, the "heavy primaries" begin to appear: gigantic packets of energy moving with almost the speed of light, each carrying enough power to start a shower of a million lesser particles.

The space doctors know very little at present about the effect that this blast of energy will have upon the sensitive jelly in human body cells. What they do know is not reassuring. When one of the great primaries passes through a photographic plate, it communicates some of its energy to the sensitive emulsion. Ions (electrified particles) are formed, and these spread out in a broad, dense band, turning crystals of silver bromide into metallic silver. All this is on a microscopic scale, but living cells are microscopic too. Many cells that are pierced by these ice picks striking out of space will certainly die, and when too many cells in a tissue die, the tissue becomes unhealthy.

Another possible effect of increased cosmic-ray bombardment is a higher rate of mutation because of damaged genes in reproductive cells. There is an unpleasant possibility that men who spend considerable periods of time above the atmosphere may return to earth to father stillborn or deformed children.

The space doctors keep their fingers crossed on this disquieting point. They have sent live mice and monkeys on rocket trips up to the realm of the cosmic rays and have recovered several of each species apparently unhurt. Some of the mice, in fact, have mated and produced normal litters. This is somewhat encouraging, but neither mice nor monkeys went higher than 36 miles, and their brush with the cosmic rays lasted only a few minutes. Since the effect of cosmic-ray bombardment is certainly cumulative, a long flight on a space cruiser or a tour of duty on a satellite station may damage a man's health or his hope of posterity.

One element of uncertainty is the fact that no one knows how many cosmic rays pass through space well away from the earth. The earth's magnetic field deflects many of them, so certain types may be more numerous beyond the range of its influence.

Another source of doubt is the inability of existing laboratory equipment to generate particles as energetic as the cosmic primaries. Until this can be done, their effect on human tissue cannot be predicted accurately.

So the experts disagree about the cosmic rays. Some of them seem to believe that the hazard is not great, or at least not great enough to compare with worse space hazards. Others take cosmic rays much more seriously. Dr. Herman J. Schaefer of the U.S. Naval School of Aviation Medicine, Pensacola, Florida, believes that they may make it legally unwise for air lines to fly their passenger ships at 90,000 feet. Their lawyers might have trouble in proving that the illness of a passenger or the malformation of a baby begotten after the flight was not due to cosmic rays.

This whole subject is under vigorous study. Data about the cosmic rays is accumulating rapidly as rockets and balloons carry more effective instruments up to their playground. The more powerful cyclotrons now under construction will be able to generate respectable primaries so that they can be studied under controlled laboratory conditions. When all the new reports have been digested, man may learn whether his space pioneers will struggle off the earth only to be withered or genetically damaged by cosmic rays.

12

ZERO GRAVITY

The oddest terror of space—weightlessness—is often treated in comic strips and in space fiction as a frolicsome amusement. Its official name is "zero gravity," and it is no joke. Ever since their fish ancestors crawled out of the sea, humans have been adjusted to the normal gravitational field that exists at the surface of the earth. Their legs are designed to support them against its down-pulling force. Their bodies are packed with senses to measure its effects. Their brains use gravitation as a frame of reference to tell what their bodies are doing. Loud alarm bells ring throughout the nervous system whenever a change of gravitational intensity warns of a stumble or a fall.

All land animals are hitched to the frame of gravitation, but man is especially sensitive to it. His more recent ancestors were arboreal, swinging through the trees like gibbons or orang-utans. For them the ground below was an ambushed enemy, forever waiting to smash their falling bodies.

To guard against this ever-present threat of death, nature provided the humanoid apes with an unusually rich array of gravity-responsive senses to detect instantly the apparent cessation of gravitation which comes at the start of a fall. At this danger signal, their bodies declared a state of desperate emergency. Their hearts pumped faster; their muscles tightened; their hands clutched; their brains raced desperately to find some means of escaping disaster.

Humans have inherited much of this apparatus, although they do not need it as much as their ape ancestors did. Their nervous systems still respond with overwhelming intensity to the threat of a fall. Since the apes came down from the trees, not many of their descendants have died from falls, but the terror is still with them. Everyone has experienced the "falling nightmare," which is a relic of the time, a million years ago, when each baby humanoid lived in constant terror of falling out of a tree.

Gravitation is still one of the world's great mysteries, but its practical effects are very well understood. Its pulling force is felt only when it is resisted. When a man is standing firmly on the ground, gravity pulls him downward. The ground presses upward, and the gravity-sensitive receptors in his muscles and other tissues report the stresses developed by the conflict of the two forces. When he holds out an arm, for instance, his gravity receptors measure the earth's pull trying to draw it down. His nervous system tells the proper muscles to resist that pull.

When a man's body slants a little away from the vertical, as it is doing continually, a whole chain of receptors—some of them very sensitive ones in the inner ear—report the slight maladjustment to gravity. Appropriate muscles go into action and by delicate movements restore the body to the vertical.

No matter how a man's body is disposed, either standing, sitting, lying or in motion, his brain gets continuous reminders of gravitation. When he is sitting, his buttocks report the reassuring presence of the chair. When he walks or runs, he is kept upright through gravity reports about the positions of all his bodily members.

These reports are based on the standard value of gravity—1 G at the surface of the earth. Man and his ancestors have lived so long in this standard gravitational field that any variation in it causes all kinds of trouble. The internal organs, for instance, are supported by elastic tissues. If the strength of gravity increases appreciably, they are pulled out of position. The circulation system, too, is designed to work properly in a 1-G field. In a stronger field, the blood runs into the lower parts of the body where the blood-containing tissues swell up to accommodate it. This draws blood out of the brain, which may cease to work or even die because of lack of oxygen-bearing blood.

Increases of gravitation are familiar enough to anyone who has ridden in an airplane or in any fast-moving vehicle. When an airplane banks to round a turn, the centrifugal force of its turning motion causes a gravity increase of a fraction of a G. In fast military airplanes that make sharp turns, the pilot may feel 5 Gs or more. Every part of his body seems to weigh five times as much as normal. His cheeks and jaw pull down; his belly seems to be swelling to the bursting point; his

Pilots have learned what to do in a high-gravity field. If enough blood flows into his legs and abdomen, he "blacks out," going blind temporarily. A few more Gs make him unconscious, and this kind of unconsciousness turns quickly to death.

This effect is familiar and has been studied in detail. The effects of high G forces can be simulated in the laboratory by means of centrifuges which whirl men around like fast-moving merry-go-rounds. Aviation-medicine experts have learned how many Gs the average man can take, and they have developed special clothing that enables him to take more without ill effects. These "G suits" are nothing but tight-fitting garments that can be made even tighter by means of rubber bladders when it is necessary. They keep too much blood from flowing into the legs and the abdomen, and so protect the pilot against blackouts and unconsciousness.

hands and forearms feel as if they were made of lead.

The strain does not last long, only while the airplane is turning sharply or pulling up out of a dive. The pilot merely sits tight, takes care that the Gs do not become too numerous and watches carefully for the signs of an incipient blackout. His reflexes have become accustomed to high-G conditions. His brain does not interpret the additional pull on his arms or the increase of pressure on his buttocks as signs that his bodily weight has actually increased. This adjustment is not difficult, because an increase of apparent weight due to a rise of G forces had never been interpreted as danger signal by the body's deep-down reflexes. But a sudden decrease of Gs is another matter entirely.

When the support is removed from under a human body, its gravity receptors have nothing to push against. They feel zero gravity, no Gs at all. They report this condition, and the central nervous system comes to the immediate and alarming conclusion that the body is falling. During the millions of years that man and his ancestors have lived on the surface of the earth, a free fall has been the only condition that could produce a sensation of zero gravity.

Free falls are dangerous not only to baby apes tumbling out of a tree, but to all animals that live in a strong gravitational field. As soon as the body feels zero gravity, the central nervous system declares a state of emergency. Everything stops while the body deals with the crisis. Even a very brief "fall," such as stepping in the dark from an unexpected curbstone, can touch off this alarm reaction. A real fall of a few feet makes the nervous system jangle like the bells of a battleship calling its crew to their battle stations.

When a rocket takes off from the earth headed for space or an orbit, the crew will feel a rapid fluctuation of G conditions. In von Braun's rocket, for instance, the force of gravity will rise to several peaks, the highest of them 9 Gs. Then, when the motors cut off and the rocket is traveling freely on its orbit through space, the crew will feel no gravity at all. They will be in a zero-gravity field and will remain in it until they turn on the motors again, or until their ship returns to the edge of the atmosphere.

When the space doctors at Randolph Field try to predict the effect of all this on von Braun's crews, they are not much worried by the 9-G peak. This force would kill a man quickly if he were sitting upright so that the blood could run out of his brain. It might also kill him by displacing his internal organs, stopping his heart or rupturing delicate tissues. But if he lies on his back on a mattress carefully shaped to fit the contours of his body, he can take 9 Gs for a brief period. He will not be comfortable, say the space doctors, but he will survive.

What worries the space doctors is not the brutal, crushing force of 9 Gs, but the intangible, psychological effect of no Gs at all. When a man enters a zero-gravity field, he loses his most basic frame of reference, the familiar pull or gravitation. The real trouble will not come from minor nuisances, such as bumping one's head against the ceiling or having to drink through a straw because water will not flow out of its glass. The trouble will come from the fact that the body no longer knows which end is up or how its members are disposed. In slightly technical language, it "loses its orientation," and orientation (knowing where you are) is the most essential thing that a body must know.

In the normal 1-G field at the surface of the earth, a continual stream of reports comes to the central nervous system from the gravity receptors all over the body. By reporting the gravity pull on all the body's parts, they tell the central nervous system what each part is doing.

A man in the dark, for instance, does not need to look at his hand to find out whether it is hanging at his side or stretched out in front of him. He knows whether he is standing up or lying down. He can even walk with confidence, and walking is a complex operation. The gravity-measuring activities of his receptors enable him to do all these things, and in a zero-gravity field, all their measurements will fall to zero.

The space doctors are not able to predict exactly how the central nervous system will react to this sudden cessation of gravity information. They do not think the effect will be good, and it may be violently bad. An immediate effect may be nausea. Seasickness is caused by the lessening of gravity, due to the motion of a ship. "Space-sickness," due to complete absence of gravity, may be even more violent.

The body can, and presumably will, get over such effects, but it will miss the gravity reports in much more serious ways. When a man in a zero-gravity field tries to reach out and pick up a pencil, he will first have to look at his hand to find out where it is. Then, watching his hand closely, he will guide it to the pencil. The motion of his hand toward the pencil will, by reaction, move his whole body backward. There will be no friction to keep him anchored to the floor.

If he stoops, his hips will rise upward. If he threshes his legs wildly to recover some connection with a solid object, he will not know what his feet are doing until he gets a look at them. His gravity receptors will not report whether his legs are vertical or horizontal. If he makes a leap to recover himself and manages to find some solid object to press his feet against, only his eyes will tell him whether his struggles have set him sailing across the room, his skull headed for a wall.

Space-travel optimists like to point out that the human nervous system is an adaptable instrument. They are sure that it can learn to orient itself and co-ordinate bodily movements without any help from gravity receptors. This may be true. The body has a few orienting senses, including some of the balancing organs in the inner ear, that do not depend entirely on gravitation. Perhaps they can be trained to take over the entire orienting job, leaving the overburdened eyes to their proper functions.

The space doctors are not at all sure about this. Both orientation and bodily movements depend on a vast array of deeply imbedded reflexes that are triggered by reports from the gravity receptors. Switching these reflexes to other sources of information cannot be done quickly, certainly not efficiently, and perhaps not at all.

Until it is done, the men in the gravity-free space ship will be almost as helpless as jellyfish stranded on a beach. They can move, but to little purpose. They will have to watch each part of their bodies to see what it is doing. Even if their nervous systems do not fall into helpless panic, as some of the experts fear that they may, they will be in no mood for navigational tasks that would stump the entire faculty of a technical institute.

Space-travel enthusiasts seldom appreciate fully these unpleasant possibilities. The less responsible of them prefer to think of life at zero gravity as an exhilarating and entertaining experience. Others admit that gravity is desirable but only to keep loose objects in place and to make soup behave. They do not like to think that zero gravity may drive space men crazy or reduce them to fumbling helplessness, like men with bad nervous diseases.

According to some of the space doctors, the worst psychological effects of zero gravity will be felt when the space men are asleep, or trying to sleep. When a human brain slips over the brink of unconsciousness, the higher parts of it, which contain the conscious will and the fruits of recent training, abdicate their power over the nervous system. The deeper reflexes do not abdicate. They bide their time until sleep has freed them from conscious supervision.

Then all sorts of ancient fears may creep out of dark corners and race through the brain as loud nightmares. There is the familiar nightmare of being chased, which probably comes from the time when man's ancestors were weakly armed primates who had to fear leopards and tigers. There is the nightmare of being naked in some public place. This is much more recent but sometimes no less distressing.

Most common is the falling nightmare, that relic of the days when the baby apes so often fell out of their trees. Normally it vanishes as soon as the victim awakes and feels the familiar support of his bed or the ground beneath him.

But in the space ship under zero gravity, the falling sensation is a constant companion. Awake or asleep, the space men will feel that they are falling. During their waking hours, their conscious minds can tell their reflexes not to worry about it, but when they fall to sleep and their conscious minds, tuckered out by tremendous labors, take a well-deserved rest, their reflexes may give the "falling" alarm.

Then nightmares will race through their brains, and they will not cease obediently as soon as the man awakes. He will feel no gravity to tell him that he is not falling. It may be quite a little time before his "waking nightmare" has quieted down. The space doctors do not know how many of such experiences a human brain can stand without going haywire. They suggest that it might be advisable to include a space psychiatrist in every rocket crew.

The worst feature of the weightlessness problem is that zero gravity can not be simulated on the earth except for very short periods. When a man jumps off a chair, he feels zero gravity for a small fraction of a second. When he dives off a springboard he feels it for a little longer. These periods are too short, and if an experimenter jumps from a greater height, he either hurts himself or has to use a parachute. Then he does not feel weightlessness. The air is supporting him through the parachute, and gravity is working again.

The only other possibility is to make a fast airplane fly in a curve with the convex side of the curve pointing upward. If this is done properly, and it is not easy, the centrifugal force of the turning will exactly balance the earth's gravitation. For a short period the pilot is weightless, and loose objects in his cockpit float around in the air just as they would in a space station traveling on its orbit.

The trouble with this experiment is that it lasts too short a time, and the pilot has too many other things on his mind. The few pilots who have done this stunt have made only vague and confused reports. They are sure of only one thing—that the sensation of weightlessness is extremely disconcerting.

Dr. Hubertus Strughold, head of Randolph Field's Division of Space Medicine, tried another experiment, using himself as the victim. While working for the German Luftwaffe during World War II, the Herr Doktor decided to test the saying that "a pilot flies with the seat of his pants." He anesthetized his buttocks with injections of novocaine and had a pilot take him up in a plane and do what he calls "loopings." His sensations during the loopings were unpleasant to a degree. As he sat on his numbed buttocks, the sky and the ground went around in a horribly willful manner. Though he had flown in all kinds of airplanes and done all kinds of stunts, he could not keep track of his motions. The gravity reports that his brain expected from his posterior did not arrive, leaving him as disoriented as a fish in a whirlpool.

A great deal more work and experience, the space doctors agree, will be needed before human psychological reactions to zero gravity can be predicted with confidence. Until then, it will not be wise to count on too great efficiency from the crew of a space ship. It may be necessary to design a rocket that can make an entire flight, including a safe return, under automatic controls. The behavior of men who ride in this vehicle can be recorded and studied. If they break down psychologically or fall into helplessness, they will have at least a chance of returning alive.

13

ROCKY SPACE

Space well away from the earth, say one thousand miles above its surface, is commonly considered a vacuum and is spoken of as such. This is not exact. The word *vacuum* means empty, and space is by no means empty. Ordinary barometers carried up into it will read zero, but this means only that they are not sensitive enough to feel the matter around them.

Astronomers agree that interplanetary space is filled with a very thin gas made up of individual molecules revolving around the sun on orbits of their own. There are dust particles, too, like little planets, and these can be seen under favorable circumstances as the Zodiacal Light, a faint, ghostly glow reaching out from the sun in the plane where the planets revolve. Such dust and gas is the stuff of which the planets were made. When the solar system was formed, the dust and gas were left behind like scattered leaf fragments on a well-raked lawn.

Even beyond the frontiers of the solar system, space is not wholly empty. Interstellar space probably has enough matter in it to equal in mass all the stars together. Even intergalactic space, those dark and lonely reaches tens of thousands of light years from the nearest star, is inhabited thinly by solitary atoms, mostly of hydrogen. According to one theory of cosmology, that of "continuous creation," they are forever being created in the cold and quiet depths of intergalactic space. They come in some unknown way from some unknown plane of reality; then in a few billion years they move together, condensing gradually into stars and galaxies.

Space travelers need not worry about the gas in space. Even within the solar system, where it is comparatively dense, it is still too thin to impede their ships or affect them in any way. But the larger particles are another matter. For voyagers into space, they are like the uncharted reefs that so often wrecked the ships of sixteenth-century navigators.

Astronomers do not know how many larger particles there are in an average cubic mile of space. Their number is probably low, but this does not mean that the danger of collision with them is also low. A space ship moves rapidly and therefore it "sweeps out" a large volume of space per second. If it has a frontal area of one hundred square feet and is moving at ten miles per second, it sweeps out a cubic mile of space in about eight hours, hitting every particle in it. Since most of the particles are moving even faster, the collision rate will be higher than this, and even very small particles can do considerable damage.

So the highway of space, which looks as free of obstructions as a deep, reefless ocean, is actually crowded with hazards to space navigation. Somewhat the same situation develops over an airport in soupy weather. Many cubic miles of air can be dangerously crowded by only a dozen fast-flying aircraft circling in the vicinity.

The speeding reefs of space are of all sizes, from fine dust up to asteroids. Once in a great while, an unusually large body smashes into the earth's atmosphere and roars through it for hundreds of miles like an incandescent freight train. Most of its substance is washed away by friction with the air and turned into dust or gas. Fragments of these "fireballs" that do reach the earth can be sold at good prices to museum-backed scientists who cherish them as the only available specimens of interplanetary matter.

Bodies large enough to reach the ground are much too rare to rate as serious space hazards. But smaller interplanetary objects that turn to dust completely before they get to the surface are not rare at all. The more they are studied, the more numerous they appear to be.

Most of the world's technically educated people now

live in great cities or near them, and the only sky they see is a murky dome reflecting the pinkish neon glare of the lights below. Stars are few in such a sky. Even in distant suburbs or country resorts, street lights and auto headlights reflect so much glare from the sky that they blot out most of the stars.

For a really good look at the space above his head, a person should go to a place—if he can find one—where no street lights are in sight. He should lie on his back looking upward on a clear and moonless night. As the strange chemistry of his eyes brings them to full sensitivity, more and more stars will appear. At last he will see the swarming multitudes that he has read about in literature that was written before man-made lights could compete with the lights of the sky. In arid regions where the air is often wondrously clear, the brightest stars will glow in colors—yellow, blue and red. Not many civilized moderns have seen the colored stars. Even a single street light bleaches their Technicolor to uniform black and white.

Most men looking upward under such conditions with dark-adapted eyes will probably be amazed to see how many of the stars are moving. Only a few bright "shooting stars" will cross the sky, but between these brilliant invaders he will see many fainter streaks of light crisscrossing the blackness. Behind them will be fainter streaks like almost invisible scratchings on worn glass. He is looking, then, at the outermost fringe of the atmosphere, which is bombarded day and night by the tiny particles, fiercely and deadly swift, that rain down out of space. On some nights the bombardment is heavy. On other nights it dies away as if the enemy in the sky had run out of ammunition.

A few years ago, only a handful of specialized astronomers took much interest in meteors. They had no practical effect on man or man's activities. But when aircraft and missiles began their climb toward the top of the atmosphere, meteors became important for half a dozen different reasons. For one thing, they offered information about the top of the atmosphere, and such information is vital. Man's new and terrible weapons —the long-range guided missiles—will travel at altitudes where the meteors sparkle and die, and the conditions that the missiles meet there will affect them profoundly on their baleful journeys.

So a sudden rush of military money deluged the meteor observers, who had been the poorest of the scientific poor. They had been sitting on hilltops counting meteor trails with their naked eyes or trying to photograph them with homemade cameras. They begged great observatories for photographic plates that happened to have meteor trails streaking across them. They collected meteor fragments and developed an elaborate science of space geology, inventing special names (all ending with the termination *ite*) for each of the unearthly minerals that meteorites contain. No one in the meteor business had serious money to spend, and few believed that their pleasant little science might be smirched with practicality. Then to their amazement they found that military treasuries would finance without limit any projects that they could devise.

Meteors are now observed and studied with an expensive array of elaborate apparatus. One of their effects is to create electrified particles in the air that they pass through. These ionized trails persist long after the meteor's luminous streak has died away, and since they reflect radar waves, they can be picked up by radar just as if they were aircraft. So in many places great radars stare at the sky all day and all night, and the faces of their oscilloscopes show the crisscrossing trails of meteors. Strong trails hang in the air for many minutes two hundred miles above the earth. As they drift slowly across the sky, they show how the thin winds are blowing on the edge of space. Such information is vitally important to men who plan to send guided missiles cruising halfway around the earth in the little-known top of the atmosphere where the meteors play.

Another kind of meteor study is done in places like New Mexico where the air is clear and space hangs close overhead. Two cameras specially designed for meteor photography are parked on patches of dark desert many miles apart. They look like clumsy mortars of Civil War days, but inside their graceless bodies are amazing optical systems that combine both mirrors and lenses and can catch the faintest streaks of light in a wide patch of sky. Revolving shutters spin rapidly in front of the lenses, and their speed is synchronized accurately over a radio channel connecting the cameras.

The cameras normally peer at the same patch of sky,

so they photograph the same meteor trails from different angles. When the plates are developed, the altitude of the trails can be estimated by triangulation. Across each meteor streak are narrow black bands made by the revolving shutter as it passes in front of the camera. Since the time between each passage of the shutter is known with extreme accuracy, the distance between the bands tells how fast the meteor was traveling. When it first enters the air, the bands are far apart; then they come closer and closer together as the meteor slows down and dies.

Analysis of the plates, which is done with electronic computers, tells how many meteors enter the earth's atmosphere. It also tells their direction and their speed. Their size can be computed from their brilliance and persistence, and much can be learned about the composition of the meteors and about the density and motion of the air that they pass through.

Another tribe of meteor observers works in chemical laboratories. With delicate apparatus, they analyze sediments from the bottoms of the oceans or from tanks of rain water or even from gutters that collect the run-off from roofs of public buildings. They are looking for the remains of burned-up meteors, which eventually filter down to the earth in the form of fine dust. If they can measure the rate of deposit, they can estimate with some accuracy the amount of cosmic material that the earth sweeps up.

Another kind of meteor counting, even less direct, is done by studying the conditions that are known to exist in the high atmosphere. Part of the energy of the meteor bombardment goes into heating the air; another part is expended in creating ionized particles. Both the temperature and the ionization can be measured in various ways and so the energy of the meteors can be estimated. This method is not accurate at present, but as man learns more about the high atmosphere, he will also learn more about the meteors that help to keep it hot and ionized.

Some of the meteor information that has been gathered so far is secret and will remain so. Since there is reason to hope that the Russians do not possess the means of accurate meteor study, it would not be wise to tell them what reefs and shoals their missiles will encounter if they ever rise from Siberia headed toward the United States. But "uncleared" space navigators have been given some data to work with. They can calculate with fair accuracy (if they choose to do so) how their space ships will interact with meteors in space.

Meteors are believed to come from two, or perhaps three, sources. Most of the largest and solidest ones— those that sometimes pass through the atmosphere and hit the surface of the earth—are believed to be the remains of a planet that once revolved around the sun between Mars and Jupiter. Perhaps there were two such bodies that collided long ago, or perhaps a single planet broke up for some unknown reason. (One space-fiction theory is that it was blown up by the Martians as a drastic act of interplanetary war.)

At any rate the orbit between Mars and Jupiter is

now filled thinly with asteroids, the largest of which, Ceres, is some five hundred miles in diameter. The rest range sharply downward in size until they become too small to be seen with even the finest telescopes. Presumably there are innumerable small ones like loose mountains revolving around the sun, and among them must be swarms of cosmic gravel and dust. Most of this gritty stuff stays on its orbital reservation, but some of the fragments wander eccentrically over most of the solar system. Those that blunder too near the earth are caught by the trap of its gravitational field and are sucked down to flaming death in its atmosphere or on its surface.

All the meteorite fragments that have been picked up for scientists to study are believed to have come from this source. Some of them are made of a tough nickel-iron alloy that is thought to resemble the metallic core of the earth. Others are "stones" made of silicates like those that predominate in the earth's crust. Intermediate types have globules or crystals of metal embedded in a stony matrix.

There is a great deal of learned argument about the planet that exploded into cosmic flak. The commonest theory is that it had a metal core surrounded by a stony crust. When it broke up, some of its fragments were made of metal, others of stone or a mixture of the two.

For hundreds of millions of years after the planet exploded, the solar system must have been unfit for navigation, with chunks as big as office buildings careening all over the place. Then little by little the surviving planets cleaned up the mess. Every million years or so, great petals of flame and dust would bloom from the side of one of them as another wandering fragment came to its end. The earth must have picked up its share of these planetesimals, but the great scars they made were quickly erased by wind and water erosion. A few of the craters can still be traced. The most famous of them and probably the most recent is the meteorite crater 4,200 feet in diameter near Canyon Diablo, Arizona, which was dug by a mass of nickel-iron whose remains still litter the site for many miles around.

Fragments of this material, which closely resembles armor plate, can be bought for 50¢ or $1 and they make fine birthday presents for space-minded boys. If the kids grow up into space pilots, they may encounter similar objects, but they will not be docile in their native space. They will be moving fifty times as fast as a rifle bullet and will contain enough energy to turn themselves and whatever they hit into white-hot gas.

Another kind of cosmic flak has an even more interesting and mysterious origin. Many of the bright meteors whose trails streak across the sky but never reach the surface of the earth seem to be made of fragile material that breaks up quickly when it comes in contact with the air. Except for those traces of sifting dust that the scientists are trying to measure, they have no samples of this brittle stuff. But they have a clue that tells them a good deal about it.

Meteors of the fragile type do not hit the atmosphere

at a constant rate like those that are believed to be remains of the departed planet. Instead they come in
bursts that last for a day or two, and all the meteors in
each burst come from the same direction. Their trails
radiate like spokes of a wheel from a single spot in the
sky, and they look as if a machine-gunner perched on
a steady star were shooting tracer bullets at the earth.
Some of these meteor showers come regularly once a
year on the same date.

The only possible explanation for this faithful peri-
odicity is that the earth passes on its orbit through
streams of meteors that move on their own orbits down
toward the sun and out again. When these orbits are
traced in space, many of them prove to coincide with
the known orbits of comets. So meteor men believe
that each shower of meteors means that the earth is
passing through the orbit of a comet and is sweeping
up loose material distributed along it. If this is true,
and it probably is, they can guess with a good deal of
confidence what that material is like.

Comets are the strangest and the least material members of the solar system. When they first appear in astronomers' telescopes, they look like fuzzy specks moving
swiftly toward the sun from dark outer space. As they
come closer, they grow the long and brilliant tails from
which their name (which means "hairy stars") was
originally derived. The tails always point away from
the sun, so astronomers decided long ago that they are
made of fine particles pushed away from the comet's
head by the pressure of sunlight.

Most of the comets move on orbits that carry them close to the sun. As they approach its fiery surface, some of them break into fragments; others disappear and are never seen again. Those that pass through the gantlet of solar light and heat whip around the sun in a tight curve and retreat with enormous speed into cold outer space. They rapidly lose their brilliance, and most of them disappear beyond the outermost planets, where they cannot be seen, even with the biggest telescope.

A special tribe of astronomers, many of whom are amateurs, concentrates upon comets, and the news of a new one arouses them all to astronomical ecstasy. They plot its orbit, measure its speed, photograph its swinging tail and analyze its light. They pray for its survival as it rounds the sun and wish it good luck and a sure return as it whips into space.

Out of the mass of information gathered by comet observers have grown several theories of what comets are made of. According to Professor Fred Whipple of Harvard, chief architect of one theory, they are rather like dirty snowballs. Out beyond the last of the planets, billions of miles from the sun, space has still a little matter in it. Some of it is fine dust particles less than one millionth of an inch in diameter. Some of it is gas: single atoms or molecules. Astronomers are not agreed whether this thin stuff belongs to the solar system or whether it is part of an interstellar cloud that the sun is passing through. At any rate it is there. It may have been thicker in the past, and most astronomers are convinced that the comets have condensed out of it. Just what makes them condense is a subject for active and sometimes acrimonious argument. One theory holds that the passage of the sun stirs up the dust cloud, making the particles collide and stick together rather in the way that the sloshing of a churn makes globules of fat in the cream grow into chunks of butter. There are other theories too, and all of them are rather difficult for non-astronomers to cope with. At any rate, sunlight is extremely weak in the distant birthplace of the comets, and the temperature of the floating matter is only a hair above absolute zero. So as the clots of particles grow, many substances that are gaseous at earthly temperatures are deposited on them as "ices." In this matrix of frozen gases are imbedded solid particles like the flecks of soot that discolor city snow. It may take billions of years for one of these dirty snowballs to grow to comet size, say 500 feet in diameter, but the universe has plenty of time at its disposal.

At first the sun's gravitation is as weak as its light, so the dirty snowballs start moving toward it with almost glacial slowness. As the years pass, their speed increases until they are plunging toward the sun in long, swift ellipses.

Sunlight is stronger now. It warms their surfaces slightly, and some of the "ices" turn into gas, detaching a few of the solid particles from the main body. This loose stuff does not wash astern like the smoke of a burning airplane; it follows faithfully the orbit of the main body. Then the growing pressure of sunlight catches the floating particles and pushes them away. They stream out behind the plunging comet and form its glowing tail. As the comet nears the sun, more of its ices evaporate and more of its particles are pushed into space. At last it develops a "head" that shines in reflected sunlight like a wide fuzzy planet, and a great shining tail many million miles long. As the comet swings around the sun, part of its material is sucked down into the fiery furnace, and some of it is blown into space by the pressure of sunlight. The volatile ices deep in the main body may be protected for a while by a layer of insulating dust, but each time that a comet swings around the sun it loses more of its ices. At last nothing remains but an empty skeleton: loose chunks of porous, fragile material barely hanging together. For a while (millions of years) they move in a great thin swarm, escorted by clouds of fine particles and molecules of gas. Eventually both chunks and particles string out along the orbit like a river running in space.

A second theory, developed by Lyttleton of Cambridge University, England, holds that comets were never large, solid bodies. Even in the depths of space, they were nothing more than swarms of small particles formed out of interstellar dust by the stirring effect of the passing sun. They become visible comets only when parts of the swarm are dense enough to be seen by reflected sunlight. The bulk of their material remains an invisible stream of cosmic pebbles and grit.

In any case, many rivers of meteors, probably connected with comets, have been charted already, and many more must exist. When the earth passes through one of them, a shower of meteors lights the sky. Even the largest chunks never reach the earth's surface. As soon as they hit the top of the atmosphere, they disintegrate like balls of popcorn shot against a stone wall.

These fast-flowing rivers of cosmic popcorn are the rocks and reefs of space, and they will be marked as hazards on the three-dimensional maps of the future space cartographers. The fragility of their material makes them no less dangerous. In the vicinity of the earth, these fragments are traveling up to forty or fifty miles per second. At this velocity nothing matters except their mass; they would have as much effect upon the skin of a space ship as if they were made of hard steel.

The third kind of cosmic particle—the micrometeorites—is only slightly known. Meteor experts had deduced from theory that very small particles that hit the atmosphere cannot give off light even if they are moving at high speed. This is because their surface is large in relation to their mass. When they hit the air, their energy turns into heat radiation; they slow down and stop without getting hot enough to become luminous. Meteor men suspected that such micrometeorites must be plentiful, but until rockets climbed into space, they had no way to observe their effects directly. Then they got something of a shock.

Some of the rockets carried internal microphones to listen for every sound and radio it back to earth. When the motor is shut off and the last of the atmosphere has been left behind, silence should be absolute except for the tickings and stirrings of the rocket's burden of instruments. But the listening microphones proved that flight through space is by no means silent.

Sharp little pings and cracklings (technically described as "high-frequency sound impulses"), rang through the rocket's skin as it floated in space. This could mean only that it was being attacked by swarms of micrometeorites. When delicately polished glass surfaces were deliberately exposed to the gnawings of these space mice, they were found to be pitted as if they had been sandblasted. Even in a few minutes, their polish was seriously dimmed. Meteor men conclude that micrometeorites too small to be detected by instruments on the earth are numerous enough to be a serious hazard of space flight.

The sum total of the meteor hazard cannot be estimated at present with entire confidence. The best that the meteor men can do is to figure vaguely on the basis of their present knowledge how many meteors a space ship of specified size is likely to encounter and what effect they will have upon it.

The material of which the flying particles are made is not very important. All of them, both hard and soft, are moving so fast that they disintegrate as soon as they hit any obstacle. What matters is the mass of the particles, and it is possible to calculate with good accuracy what effect both large and small particles will have on the skin of a space ship.

Meteors large enough to reach the surface of the

earth as solid bodies are much too rare to be worried about. An encounter with one of them would, of course, wreck a space ship completely, but such an infrequent accident can be written off, like the chance that the *Queen Mary* may be struck in mid-Atlantic by a disabled air liner. Even particles as big as B-B shot are so rare that a space ship could cruise for millions of years without hitting one of them. This is small cause for rejoicing. The particles speeding through space carry such enormous energy that they are dangerous when no bigger than grains of fine sand.

No projectile that man can shoot in his laboratories moves as fast as these fierce little specks, but the damage that they will do can be predicted by theoretical means. Meteor men figure that a particle of conservative speed (25 miles per second) need weigh only two-millionths of an ounce to penetrate sheet-aluminum alloy one-eighth of an inch thick. It will make a conical hole growing larger toward the inside, and both the meteor itself and the material removed by it will appear inside the space ship as a spray of white-hot gas. Anything near this dagger of flame will be seriously damaged, and probably a powerful shock wave will echo inside the ship. Air will rush through the hole into the vacuum outside and unless the hole is plugged promptly, the crew of the space ship will die from explosive decompression or lack of oxygen.

Most experts agree that penetrations will not be too common. They figure that a spherical space vehicle about ten feet in diameter with an aluminum skin one-eighth of an inch thick can count on cruising for a year, on the average, at the top of the atmosphere without being punctured. If it flies higher, so that it loses the earth's shielding effect, it will be in somewhat more danger. Optical surfaces attached to the space ship, and this includes windows to observe the stars, must be protected against the gnawing of micrometeorites. Long-range guided missiles on their quick dashes through space are not seriously threatened by meteors, but space ships making long voyages to a foreign planet are almost sure to have meteor trouble before they get back to their base.

At all costs, however, say the meteor men, space vehicles must avoid the thick-set reefs that lie in the orbits of comets. To cruise through a meteor stream would be like slamming an ocean liner, at night and at full speed, through a sea full of coral reefs.

The meteor hazard is most serious for satellite stations intended to circle for years round and round the earth. They will have to sail in all kinds of meteor weather, including those stormy periods that come several times each year when the earth passes through wide rivers of meteors. The stations will present very large targets, and the design of most of them makes them extremely vulnerable to meteor penetration. The flexible inflated walls of von Braun's station will certainly be punctured by very small particles.

One proposed answer to the meteor hazard is the "meteor bumper," which takes advantage of the fact that the speeding particles flash into gas as soon as they hit an obstacle. If the space ship has a sheet of thin metal about half an inch outside its main skin, a meteor will hit it first. Instead of passing through it intact as a bullet would, it will disintegrate into a spurt of hot gas. This will distribute its energy over a larger area of the inner skin, and so it will not have enough concentrated power to punch a hole through it. Partisans of this device believe that a meteor bumper one-tenth as thick as the main skin will reduce to one-tenth the probability that the space vehicle will suffer meteor puncture.

This factor of protection is not enough to keep a satellite space station from being deflated by meteors, especially when it is passing through a dense stream of them. When satellite enthusiasts are confronted by this peril, they reply rather lightly that simple engineering devices will certainly be developed to take care of it.

Satellite-station architects have spent many happy hours working out such devices. One of them is a double hull providing an open space just inside the main skin of the vehicle. It will be pressurized like the rest of the station and will contain many small plastic balloons. When a meteor punctures the main skin and air rushes out through the hole, the balloons will be drawn automatically toward the leak and will plug it before much air has had time to escape. Then a party of meteor-damage experts will patch the leak permanently.

Other space stations have airtight bulkheads with automatically closing doors like those in the watertight compartments of a battleship. When a meteor punches into one of the compartments, sensitive instruments detect the loss of air and close the doors quickly, keeping the rest of the space station from losing its air. Then men in space suits enter the vacuum of the punctured compartment to repair the hole.

All such devices, including the simple meteor bumper, added weight and complication. When space architects present their elegant designs, they hardly ever include these essentials or estimate how much they will cost in terms of burdens that must be dragged up from the distant earth. But included they must be, for without good protection from meteor puncture no satellite station can cruise on its orbit for long.

When long-range space ships take off on journeys to foreign planets, their crews may breathe somewhat easier, like deep-sea sailors delighted to leave a reef-fringed shore. The earth attracts meteors, diverting them from their normal courses, so they are probably thickest just above the atmosphere. Space navigators hope that they will not be as numerous on the high seas of space.

A long-range space ship, moreover, has freedom of maneuver while a satellite station is tied to the earth's orbit and is therefore carried helplessly right through meteor streams. The space ship may be able to avoid these fast-flowing rivers of disaster. They are not easy to chart; they crisscross through space in every possible direction and on orbits of different curvatures. When they pass close to a massive planet, they are sometimes diverted, like earthside rivers meandering over a rolling prairie.

But charting them is possible, and it may also be possible to detect their menacing presence many thousand miles ahead. When this has been done, the space ships may be able to navigate safely by steering their way among the meteor streams, like ocean liners avoiding festoons of reefs.

This security is for the future. During the early years of space exploration, many space ships will disappear utterly, like the many ships of sixteenth-century Europe that sailed into the Atlantic and were never heard from again. Their radio signals will stop, perhaps in the middle of a sentence. Perhaps the last sound to come over the channel will be the sharp crack of a shock wave echoing inside the hull. Then the books of that ship will be closed, and brief technological prayers will be said for the souls of its crew. The punctured derelict, wrecked on a rock no bigger than a grain of sand, will swing through space for millions or billions of years until it falls at last into the sun.

14

NUCLEAR DISAPPOINTMENT

Some readers may have wondered why space ships powered by atomic energy, the great gift of science to the
space-fiction writers, have not been mentioned so far.
There is an excellent reason. All responsible authorities
agree that it will be much harder to build rockets
driven by nuclear fission than warships or airplanes
driven by nuclear fission—and these are plenty hard
enough. A small chunk of uranium contains, theoretically, enough energy to toss a space ship to Mars, but
turning that energy into propulsive force in the vacuum
of space is discouragingly difficult.

Besides the conventional problems (shielding, high
temperature, etc.) that beset all nuclear-power projects,

the designers of nuclear-powered rockets must face an additional obstacle. An ocean-going ship moves by pushing against the water. That is, its propeller sets large amounts of water moving slowly astern. The reaction to this motion moves the ship forward. An airplane, whether it uses a propeller or a jet, does the same thing.

But a rocket moving through space has no surrounding medium to set in motion. Its motor shoots out a stream of hot gases produced by its own fuel, and the thrust developed depends on both the speed and the mass of the departing gases. The great failing of an atomic energy rocket motor is that its abundant energy is not all that it needs. In addition, it must have some mass to throw overboard; the development of energy alone is not enough. A compromise with this situation is to provide the motor with some material to heat strongly and shoot out through its tailpipe. Hydrogen is the best stuff for this purpose. Its molecules are small and light, and for complicated physical reasons they give the strongest thrust for a given temperature in the motor's heating chamber.

Even the enthusiasts now admit that this system does not look too practical. Such a motor will have to carry into space the great weight of the reactor and the shield around it, and this burden will more than cancel the advantage of the almost unlimited energy in the uranium fuel. When it runs out of hydrogen, it will be as helpless as a V-2 that has run out of oxygen and alcohol.

Many dodges have been proposed to get around this difficulty. One is to use an ion beam instead of a stream of hot gases to supply thrust. Ions are particles, say of hydrogen, that are electrically charged. If they are positive in charge, they are repelled powerfully by a positive electrical field. In certain laboratory devices they can be made to move in this way at almost the speed of light.

Such an ion beam exerts a thrust like a stream of gases propelled by high temperature. The mass of its particles may be small, but they are moving so fast that their propulsive effect (measured by mass combined with speed) may be very great.

In the ionic rockets of space doodlers, the fission of uranium yields high-tension electrical power to charge the hydrogen particles and to maintain the field that repels them from the ship. A thin trickle of hydrogen is enough to supply the flow of particles, so the ionic motor can keep blasting almost indefinitely.

The difficulties of building a motor of this sort are fantastically great, and no design proposed so far shows promise of practicality. For the time being at least, ionic rockets will have to stay in the pages of space fiction, where they are already plentiful.

A somewhat similar scheme, even more fantastic, is to use a beam of light, which also exerts thrust. The rather mysterious particles of light (photons) move at the constant and respectable speed of 186,000 miles per second, so a very small mass of light can, theoretically, give a powerful thrust. The trouble with this idea is that a propulsive light beam must be very bright indeed. The pressure of sunlight falling at noon on a city block is much less than the weight of a cigarette paper resting on one of its roofs. To lift a space ship free of the earth would take a beam a billion times brighter than full sunlight. No one knows at present how to build such a Paul Bunyan searchlight.

The nuclear-propulsion enthusiasts are not greatly discouraged by any of these difficulties. They point out that man's attainment of nuclear energy is only a little more than ten years old. There is plenty of time ahead, and almost anything can happen in another ten, or one hundred, or one thousand years. Nuclear technology is growing like the green bay tree, both in laboratories that are permitted to report their findings publicly and in secret ones like Los Alamos.

It is not impossible, say the space-travel optimists, that some nuclear process that can be utilized for propulsion has been discovered already, and is being kept secret. So they watch romantic Los Alamos like a pack of children on Christmas Eve, circling around the guarded presents under the Christmas tree.

15

POWER FOR THE GLORY

It is not good to allow skeptics and faint hearts to hold the floor uninterruptedly. Like the early radios that broke into howls just when their voices were loudest and clearest, the skeptics can obscure the issue if permitted too much scope. A movement as long-range as man's spread into space includes positive pulls that draw it forward as well as negative obstacles that tend to hold it back.

Let us grant freely that escape from the earth will be difficult, dangerous and extremely expensive on anything less than a war-waging scale. Then let us put these obstacles in proper perspective. The best way to do this is to drop backward in time to the average birth

date of men who have reached senatorial age. Not
many remember, except with juvenile rosiness, the year
1900. Perhaps people were as happy then as they are
now; it is hard to prove that happiness is not a sub-
jective constant. But certainly not many citizens of 1900
could imagine the world that we live in today.

Life moved then with slow sedateness, freighted down
by huge Sunday dinners, the leisurely clatter of horse-
cars, the soporific drone of sermons and the buzz of
flies born in plentiful manure and safe from DDT.
Telephones were scarce and wonderful and had only
begun to disband the armies of messenger boys. Autos
were rare "horseless carriages," and they were much less
dependable than the horse-drawn ones. The fastest vehicles were railroad trains, which clattered precariously
at a mile a minute. Nothing important flew through
the air except birds and bats and balloons.

All this is mere gadgetry. There have been much
more profound changes since the year 1900. The human
race has acquired new power, which both transcends
and generates gadgetry. In 1900 few human brains received any training above the level of artisan skills and
bare literacy. A large proportion of the few who did
get higher education became lawyers, clergymen and
other devotees of tradition. Even in advanced countries,
only a microscopic fraction of the available brains were
put in touch with the fast-accumulating body of human
knowledge. The vast majority plodded along as igno-
rant of science and technology as their ancestors had

been in the ghost-ridden Middle Ages when they wore leather pants and no underclothes.

This darkness of the average mind was inevitable in 1900. Even in lands of plenty like the United States, the techniques of getting a living did not permit the average boy to give much time to education. He had to go to work right out of grammar school, scratching food out of the earth with muscle-power tools or practicing the handicrafts that still produced the bulk of manufactured goods. If the millions of young Americans who are now in high school or college should be dropped back to 1900, most of them would be at work, and doing jobs that could bring them no knowledge and only a slow increase of traditional skills.

Since 1900, this barrier has been broken through, like the great stone walls that once surrounded the hearts of medieval cities, and which can now be traced as ring-shaped parks inside the nearest suburbs. The productivity of modern living techniques has risen to a point where most young men can be spared from production until they have had time to train their brains. This has multiplied many times the number of active brains in each advanced country. The growth of knowledge and technology no longer depends upon the brains of a few men, who were generally the sons of wealth or had some other fortuitous advantage. In the United States at least, nearly every young man who wants and can absorb information is able to get it somehow.

The result has been what scientists call a geometrical

increase in technological knowledge. As more brains participate in creating machines and methods to lighten the labors of man, they free still more brains for the learning process. These in due course get into the game in greater numbers and on a higher level. Their accomplishments raise in turn the productivity of the average man and make it easier for his sons to open their minds to knowledge.

In the entire United States of 1900, there were probably not enough trained technical brains to staff a single great laboratory, such as the Schenectady research center of the General Electric Company. Now the country is full of such places. They are springing up, complete with cyclotrons, wind tunnels and tangles of chemical apparatus, in places like the cotton states, where in 1900 there was hardly anything resembling high technology.

This curve of popular technical knowledge is still sweeping upward, growing steeper every year. Both government and private industry are screaming for technically trained men, and each year the growth of the nation's productivity releases more young brains for technical training. The ceiling of this spiral is not yet in sight. There is no lack of mental raw material. Brains fit for the highest training can be found in every social, economic and racial level of the American population.

The same development is going on in other countries, especially the British Commonwealth. If the human race should decide to make the great effort of expanding beyond the earth, it will need even more of these technically trained brains, and more will be forthcoming. This is a happy condition that has never existed before.

Another startling development since 1900 is the rapid welding of large numbers of human beings into closely co-operating units. Part of this is due to improvements of communication. There were telegraphs in 1900, but they were used by few. Telegrams were feared almost superstitiously; they often brought news of death. Travel by railroad or ship over moderate distances was not much slower than it is today, but it was expensive and uncomfortable, and few people traveled. Radio, television, motion pictures and other means of mass communication that make large numbers of people think in unison had not been imagined. Newspapers covered only their small home territories. There were few high-quality national magazines, and their circulations were trifling. The trade and technical press, which now penetrates every cranny of the nation, was almost nonexistent. Few Americans could have read such difficult stuff, and fewer would have made the effort.

The lack of communication and interest in things at a distance made the prevailing pattern of life limited and parochial. There were great corporations, but they were centralized chiefly through simple financial control. If they had widely separated parts, these were more independent than they are today and tended to serve their immediate neighborhoods.

The close-knit corporations that cover the entire nation at present and keep in intimate unity by means of telephone tie-lines, teletype circuits, air mail, house organs and fleets of private airplanes were inconceivable then. So were chain-store systems and mail-order houses with the purchasing power of entire states. No corporation had the resources, mobility or imagination to tackle the enormous enterprises that many of them take in stride today. If the federal government had wanted an atom bomb in 1900, it could not have found a private corporation to take on any of the baffling tasks involved in making one.

The federal government in 1900 was, of course, much too feeble to conceive of any such enterprise. It was strained to its limit by the comparatively small job of digging the Panama Canal. Now it could dig ten such canals per year and not exhaust its own credit or the nation's supply of skilled manpower.

The project of flying into space would have been inconceivable in 1900, not only in a technical way, but also in an organizational way. Each task would have had to have been farmed out among thousands of little outfits. The federal government itself would have been inadequate. It was staffed almost exclusively by men without technical knowledge, and its power to mobilize money and men for anything except war was less than that of many present-day corporations. The social mechanism necessary for an enterprise on the scale of space flight just did not exist. It does today.

Probably the greatest change since 1900 has been in the human spirit itself. The people of the late nineteenth century were confident in some ways. They believed in material progress, but what they meant by this phrase was that the world could potentially enjoy more of the blessings that it knew already. What the world needed to do, in their view, was to follow certain well-known rules and everything would be all right.

Since then there has been an extraordinary revolution in thought. Einstein's theory of relativity knocked some of the props from under man's conception of the universe. Modern astronomy knocked out others. Modern chemistry destroyed great industries and created more. Old skills became useless and new skills, which were usually mental, became crying necessities. Nearly every barrier to man's unlimited growth was broken through. The culminating point so far came only ten years ago, with the development of the atomic bomb. This triumph convinced the general public that "science can do anything."

Space-travel enthusiasts point to all these developments since 1900 as favoring their project. For the first time the world, and even the United States alone, has something like enough trained technical brains. It has vigorous organizations, both private and public, that grasp eagerly at any great task. Most important of all, it has an indomitable confidence which has not been seen in the world since the time of the ancient Greeks.

"Unbreakable" rules have been broken. "Eternal laws" have been proved temporary. There still are plenty of voices that try to tell the human spirit that it must look to the past for wisdom. Such gray advice is not heeded except in a purely formal way. The heads of governments and corporations may pretend to a pious respect for the eternal verities, but they tell their researchers to go right ahead and destroy any verity that gets in their way.

What has been done so far, the space philosophers ask, with this enormous increase of human power and knowledge? It has changed the face of the earth, to be sure, and changed the traditional ways of human life. But during the last fifty years, the bulk of human energy and productivity has been poured down the rat holes of two world wars. Now it is running in a vast river down a third rat hole of preparing for war. What will happen, the space philosophers ask, if this rat hole were to be closed, like the penstock of a powerhouse that takes the whole flow of a river? Will the river stop its flow, which has been increasing by a factor of ten in each generation?

Not likely, say the space philosophers. The new surplus energies of the human race are a dangerous force that demands employment. They will wreck any social system that denies them an outlet, and what better outlet could there be than the inspiring project of colonizing the solar system, and perhaps empty space itself?

So the true space-travel enthusiasts brush aside such minor squabbles as the controversy between von Braun and the guided-missile experts. If the human race, they say, were to devote to space flight only a small fraction of the money and effort that it invests in war, rockets will leave the earth, satellites will circle the earth, space ships will explore the solar system and perhaps find places for colonies that will surpass their mother planet in accomplishment, as colonies often do. Men may even find that his proper habitat, where he can develop to his fullest extent, is space itself.

Let us leap over the immediate obstacles, the space philosophers say. Let us suppose that we have the necessary money and can take the necessary time to reach the highway of space. Then let us make great plans, for only plans that are blindingly great can call forth the necessary effort.

16

TELESCOPES IN SPACE

Cautious space-travel enthusiasts, to whom a full program of space colonization seems too ambitious, believe that an effort should be made to reach a limited objective. Many of the men, for instance, who work on guided missiles are deeply conscience-stricken about their warlike purposes. They love their beautiful and intelligent mechanisms and hate to think that their ultimate aim is to destroy some city halfway around the earth. They like to dream that they may accomplish some better purpose, preferably furthering the development of the whole human race. One project that meets this spiritual test is the construction of space observatories.

As every astronomers knows and frequently states

with feeling, the surface of the earth is a poor place from which to observe the universe. On a clear day or night the atmosphere looks transparent, but this is a cruel illusion. Human eyes evolved underneath the atmosphere, and so they see by a special kind of radiation (visible light) that penetrates the air fairly easily. To most of the radiation that comes from the sun or the stars the atmosphere is as opaque as an ocean of ink.

Astronomers sometimes tantalize themselves by imagining the whole great spectrum of radiation that beats upon the earth from the sun and outer space. It starts at one end with very long waves like those that are broadcast by radio stations. Next come the shorter waves that are used in radars; next come infrared (heat) waves, followed by visible light, ultraviolet, X-rays and gamma rays.

Most of these wave lengths are completely blocked off by the earth's atmosphere. Through one "window" in it come radio waves that range in length from one millimeter to thirty meters. Through another window come visible light and a little infrared and a little ultraviolet. That is all, and it is a small fraction of the total. The rest never reach the earth's surface. Even the part that does enter man's instruments has a rough passage and arrives in terrible shape.

Those bright, clear nights when the stars flash like diamonds are almost useless to astronomers. The twinkling means that the air is full of turbulence. Its irregularities bend the light from the stars and make their images tremble and jump. In a powerful telescope they look like dancing motes, and pictures taken of them are hopelessly blurred. On such nights the astronomers go to bed in disgust. Even on the nights of best seeing, the stars do not hold still. Even rather small telescopes cannot use their full magnification. When they do, the stars jump around too much to be observed or photographed.

All these troubles would be nonexistent in space; the faintest stars would shine as steadily as street lights, and their entire spectra would stream without damage or dimming into the instruments. Astronomers transported to a space observatory would feel like men who have been groping in a dark basement and have suddenly opened a door on the sunlit world.

Many astronomers have doodled happily with designs of telescopes to be used from satellite stations circling round the earth. The more they doodle, the better it looks to most of them. Once the problems of life on a satellite have been solved satisfactorily, it should be a fairly straightforward matter to use the satellite as an observatory.

The worst enemy of large telescopes on the earth is gravitation. As their concave mirrors turn to follow a star, the changing effect of their weight distorts them slightly, and an error of one-millionth of an inch is enough to destroy their usefulness. So the mirrors are made thick and rigid, and they are supported underneath by incredibly complicated apparatus to keep them from changing their shape as the telescope swings. All this makes the mirrors heavy, and massive mounts must be provided to carry them. The two-hundred-inch telescope on Palomar Mountain weighs five hundred tons. The part of it that does the essential optical work is a thin film of aluminum on the surface of the mirror. It weighs only a small fraction of an ounce. The rest of the five hundred tons is chiefly concerned with counteracting gravitation.

In space, of course, nothing has weight, so the mirror can be made of any thickness, and it needs no support as it turns. Since gravitation is not affecting it, it will not change its shape. Instead of five hundred tons, the mirror and tube of a two-hundred-inch space telescope need weigh only a few hundred pounds.

Another enemy of telescopes on earth is change of temperature. The great tubes must be open to the sky, and even warming or cooling them a few degrees is enough to threaten their accuracy. Telescopes in space will not be free of the temperature annoyance. If sunlight or the radiation reflected from the earth is allowed to strike their mirror or other working parts, its heat will distort them and destroy their accuracy. But shielding them should be simple. Shades made of metal foil or of thin metalized plastic film ought to be enough. They will have no weight, of course, and so they can be held in position by spidery wire supports.

The telescope's optical parts will have to be protected from micrometeorites whose continuous gnawing would soon dim their polish. This is a serious but not insoluble problem. Micrometeorites move in essentially straight lines—almost like light itself—so only those that enter the telescope tube nearly parallel to its long axis will do damage to the mirror. For certain kinds of observation it may be possible to exclude even these by stretching thin films of transparent material across the mouth of the tube and renewing them when necessary. No one can guess at present whether the impacts of micrometeorites will vibrate or displace the telescope. If they do, they will have to be screened away from it.

Great telescopes on earth are mounted on massive bearings so beautifully contrived and machined that electric motors no bigger than oranges keep them swinging with the stars. A satellite telescope will need no bearings at all. It will hang weightless in frictionless space. The slightest push will start it revolving around its own center of mass. Its operator cannot touch it without making it swing widely across the sky.

Designers of space telescopes agree that they must be operated by remote controls, preferably through radio signals sent to them from the satellite. They will be pointed in the desired direction by small flywheels or gyroscopes. Once they are pointed right, the same devices will keep them on target. Such controls can be made as delicate as necessary. There will probably be two sets—one to swing the telescope through large angles; the other, which need be no bigger than a watch, to move it gently from star to star.

Most of the telescope's work will be done photographically, and the plates will have to be changed and exposed by remote controls. New kinds of plates will have to be developed, of course, for the telescope will take pictures not only in ordinary light but also in novel wave lengths that have never entered the eye of an earth-borne telescope.

Astronomers can guess only vaguely what the pictures will show. They know that the sun sends out floods of ultraviolet that cannot be observed effectively at present, and they assume that many other stars must do the same. They suspect that the sky has many cool stars in it. Pictures taken with long-wave infrared should trace them to their hiding places. Some of them will be dying stars that have spent nearly all of their energy. Others will be infant stars—great clouds of gas and particles that have not yet grown hot enough to glow with visible light.

Astronomers believe that some stars send out hard X-rays like exploding atom bombs. These do not penetrate the earth's atmosphere, and even if they did, they could not be used to take pictures with. They would pass right through a telescope's mirror as if it were not there. But in the virtual vacuum that surrounds the space station, such rays can be detected by electronic methods. Space-borne astronomers may find that the X-ray stars are stronger and more numerous than had been supposed, and that they are powered by atomic reactions undreamed of by man.

Undoubtedly one of the great preoccupations of the space-borne astronomers will be to study the moon and the planets. For a telescope whose vision is not blurred by the earth's atmosphere, the moon will seem almost next door. Objects on it no bigger than office buildings will stand out as sharply as the lines of a new dollar bill. Photographs taken of Mars will show everything more than a few miles across. This should solve once and for all the question of whether Mars has intelligent inhabitants. A photograph of the earth in this detail would show many of the works of man.

The atmospheres of the planets, even the most distant ones, could be analyzed accurately from the satellite observatory. Space voyagers would learn what to expect when they try to explore their surfaces. Even the mysterious surface of Venus might be photographed in long heat waves struggling up through its dense, opaque atmosphere.

All the projects outlined above are the unfinished business of earth-borne astronomers. Space-borne astronomers will certainly find new problems that could not be imagined on the earth. There may be wholly new bodies in space, wholly new structures and processes. The cosmic rays may be traced to their mysterious origins. It may be possible to decide whether matter is really being created out among the galaxies. If this proves to be the case, there must be another kind of universe which is apparent to us only through the hydrogen atoms that leak out of it into ours. Perhaps the satellite-borne astronomers may be able to penetrate some little distance into this unknown plane of reality. They may find that it is more real than the "real" world we have known.

When astronomers think of such problems, which lie on the vague boundary between science and philosophy, they remember the part that astronomy—the grandfather of the sciences—has played in the history of human civilization. In the earliest days it led men out of barbarism, permitting them to predict the seasonal flow of rivers and the annual cycle of their crops. It taught them the value of systematic observation, which is the practical base of all the sciences.

Astronomy as a science disappeared when the learning of the Roman Empire turned into the superstition of the Dark Ages. A thousand years later it reappeared, stronger than ever, to lead the scientific revival that has enabled the Western European culture to dominate the world. When Galileo and his contemporaries gave Europeans a clear glimpse of the universe, the worst of their superstitious bonds broke like chains of butter.

The medieval men of learning before Galileo did not consider themselves benighted. When they argued in their universities about religious dogmas that seem utterly ridiculous to modern minds, they thought of themselves as dealing intelligently with real things. Most modern scientists have the same confident feeling. Only when they fetch up against one of the boundaries of modern knowledge do they feel doubts about the validity of their practices. Then a small persistent voice speaks to them out of the darkness. "Do events really happen because of causes?" it asks them naggingly. "Or don't they, and can you prove it?" And, "What is matter, and time, and space, and where did the universe come from, and are there other universes?"

Not only astronomers hear these questioning voices.

Mathematicians and physicists often hear them too. They suspect that the human intellect is approaching a boundary of mystery which its present tools cannot penetrate. Some of them feel that the satellite observatory may be the necessary tool, and that the information which it will bring to man may start a new scientific cycle—like the one that began with Galileo. Then the death-dealing work of the guided-missile men will be crowned in the end with spiritual justification.

17

TO OTHER PLANETS

The hopes of the more ambitious space men do not stop with satellite stations or with telescopes floating near them. They plan to cruise deep into space, far from the earth, and visit any points of interest that they can find in it.

Most of the plans for deep space voyages start with a satellite station like the one described by von Braun. The initial problems of life on such a station have presumably been licked. A sufficient stream of shuttle rockets brings up supplies, instruments and relief crews from the earth below. They also bring prefabricated parts of a space ship that can make long voyages entirely free of the earth.

This vehicle, the space men point out quickly, will not resemble at all the rocketlike objects that dart through space in the comic strips. Since it will encounter no air or other atmosphere, it does not need to be streamlined. Its shape will be determined by its internal functions, especially the fact that it will have to contain a capsule of synthetic atmosphere to keep its crew alive.

If zero gravity has proved troublesome, the space ship will have to spin, as von Braun's satellite does, to create synthetic gravity. But few space men admit that the ill effects of zero gravity will be more than temporary. The transition to weightlessness may be unpleasant, but human brains and nervous systems are flexible things. Weight is a burden, after all. Human bodies may function better when gravity no longer entangles them.

The deep-space vehicle will need a rocket motor, of course, but it need not be a big one. Shuttle rockets rising from the earth must be extremely powerful. Their job is to reach sufficient speed to maintain themselves in an orbit above the atmosphere. A space ship already in such an orbit need exert only a very small force to circle higher away from the earth. Theoretically any force will do, however small. If the thrust continues long enough, the space ship can climb little by little, circling higher above the earth until it is so far away that the earth's gravitation has become negligible.

This would take a very long time, and it is not necessary. The space planners propose to use a rocket that is strong enough to curve the space ship away from the earth in a single swoop and also give it speed enough to reach its next objective in a reasonably short time. The details of this sort of thing make fascinating reading for people who enjoy some fairly easy mathematics.

The moon is the nearest objective, of course, and nearly all space voyagers have worked out plans to reach it. Von Braun, for instance, proposes to start the voyage from his satellite station, which is already moving around the earth at 15,840 miles per hour. His moon ship will fire its rather modest rocket for two minutes and this will raise its total speed to 22,100 miles per hour. If this power maneuver has been performed correctly, the ship will reach the moon's orbit in about five days, gradually slowing down. If the moon arrives at the rendezvous when it is expected to, the space ship will circle it and return to the earth.

All the calculations and maneuvers must be exact; the moon is a small and rapidly moving target. Corrections, of course, are possible at any time, and if the ship is captured as a satellite by the moon's gravitational field, it can easily blast itself free.

Its return to the earth will be more critical. As it falls with increasing speed for 238,000 miles, it will gain sufficient velocity to shoot past the earth entirely and out on the other side to the distance of the moon's orbit. So as it approaches the earth, it will have to turn itself in space, pointing its rocket ahead of its motion. The rocket will be fired at the right moment for a sufficient period to reduce the ship's speed to that of the satellite from which it made its departure. Then if all has gone well, and the chances of error are considerable, the ship will coast close to the satellite. Its crew will put on their space suits and waft themselves across, to receive the congratulations of the satellite's garrison.

This is only one proposal. Many more can be found in the literature of space flight, which goes back to the Germans, Russians, Frenchmen and others who made their theoretical flights to the moon long before Goddard's first feeble rocket rose above Massachusetts. Arthur C. Clarke, for instance, proposes to send three rockets up from the earth. All three will stabilize themselves in an orbit five hundred miles above the surface. Two of them will be tankers to refuel the third.

Clarke proposes to approach the moon with a good deal of circumspection. He will park his fuel supply for the return journey in an orbit around it. Then his rocket will descend to the moon's surface, braking its speed against the moon's feeble gravitation by means of rocket blasts. Enough fuel will remain to leave the moon again and pick up the rest of the fuel in the nearby orbit.

Clarke admits that these operations will be hazardous, but he sees little hazard in the return to the earth. Instead of plunging boldly and red hot into the atmosphere, as von Braun's returning rockets are expected to do, his space ship coming back from the moon will merely graze the atmosphere and then shoot out into space where it can cool off. On its next descent it will be moving a little slower and can remain in the atmosphere a little longer without getting so hot. After a sufficient number of these grazing ellipses the rocket will be flying slowly enough to land like an ordinary airplane.

A voyage to Mars or Venus, or any other planet, for that matter, requires little more fuel than a trip to the moon. The earth's gravitational field extends indefinitely, but at the distance of the moon's orbit it has become so feeble that not much of it remains to impede the motion of a space ship. If the ship gets as far as the moon, a slight additional push will free it from the earth entirely.

Von Braun and a large school of astronauts propose to start their voyages to Mars or Venus from their satellite station. The trick in all interplanetary voyaging is to blast the space ship free of the earth and set it in an orbit around the sun. Then, by the judicious use of rocket power, the orbit can be moved inward or outward until it intersects the orbit of the target planet.

In the case of Mars, whose orbit lies outside that of the earth, the space ship moving around the sun needs to be speeded up a little. This will spiral it outward, away from the sun, to the orbit of Mars. In the case of Venus, which lies nearer the sun, the space ship should be slowed down. Then it will move in toward the sun until it reaches the orbit of Venus.

For the start from the satellite station, the all-important point is timing. The satellite and the space ship with it is moving around the earth at 15,840 miles per hour. The earth is moving on its own orbit at 66,600 miles per hour. For a voyage to Mars, a departure instant is selected when the satellite is moving in the same direction as the earth and therefore has a velocity of 82,440 miles per hour. A comparatively slight additional push, hardly more than is needed to go to the moon, sends it spiraling out to Mars.

In the case of Venus, the space ship will leave the satellite when its motion is opposed to the motion of the earth. Then a push that frees it from the earth's gravitation will place it in space with a velocity low enough so that it will fall in a spiral towards the sun and intersect the orbit of Venus.

During all departures for the planets, the moon is an undesirable bystander. Its position must be watched carefully or its gravitational field, though weak, will "perturb" the space ship out of its proper course. Distant planets, notably Jupiter, may have perturbing effects also, especially on voyages to Mars.

When the space ship approaches its target planet, it will be speeded up by the new gravitational field. Its procedure at this point will depend on whether it intends to land directly on the planet, or to park itself in an orbit around it, or merely to take a look and return to the earth. If the target planet has moons, as Mars has, they will stand careful watching.

Landing on a planet (and getting home again) is a problem that even the most intrepid astronauts treat with some caution. The key point to consider here is whether the target has an atmosphere. The moon and Mercury have none or virtually none. Mars has a thin atmosphere, like that of the earth at about 50,000 feet. Venus has a thick atmosphere, and the great outer planets are probably largely gaseous. The small fry of the solar system, asteroids and most of the moons of the planets, have no atmospheres. The sun, of course, has plenty; it is entirely gaseous. But even the most daring astronaut does not plan to visit the sun.

Landing on the moon (or Mercury) can be done only by using the rocket motors as brakes. The ship will turn so that its rockets are pointing toward the target. Then, as it approaches the moon's surface, its course will be adjusted by slightly off-center blasts to make it head for a comparatively level spot. The moon has mountains higher than the earth's and much more precipitous. As the ship drops down, its speed will be checked by judicious blasts from the rockets. It will land gently (it is hoped) stirring up a cloud of the fine dust with which the moon is believed to be covered.

What the astronauts will do then is somewhat conjectural. When the moon's surface is sunlit, it is uncomfortably hot, most of it being well above the boiling point of water. During the long night the surface becomes deathly cold, dropping close to absolute zero. Presumably the space men will have learned how to deal with such temperature fluctuations; they will have encountered them before on their satellite and during their voyage. In case their defenses fail, however, there is a refuge on the moon. Lunar specialists think they have detected in one of the moon's sharp ridges a tunnel that may have been blasted by a glancing meteorite. They suggest that the space men land near this and take shelter in it. By day they will be protected from the glaring sun, and at night the moon's internal heat may warm the tunnel appreciably.

The landing on the moon must be done in such a way that it does not damage the space ship; any repairs would be difficult, to put it mildly. The ship must have also enough fuel left to climb up again into space. This will not be too difficult. There will be no air to offer resistance, and the moon's gravitational field is a puny thing.

Landing on a planet with an atmosphere will be more difficult in some ways and easier in others. Such planets have strong gravitational fields or they could not hold their atmospheres. So they will suck a space ship toward them at very great speed. This speed will have to be reduced by the air-braking system. To cancel it out by firing the space ship's rockets would take almost as much fuel as to escape from the planet.

Unfortunately, a space ship constructed to float through airless space is not suitable for roaring red hot through a planetary atmosphere. Most designs of such space vehicles show fragile, spherical tanks and crew chambers connected by an open framework. This light, unstreamlined stuff would be washed away by the first brush with an atmosphere. So the more conservative astronauts plan to circle the target planet, perhaps hanging around it in a nearby orbit for a few days or weeks. After scouting it thoroughly and determining, if they can, whether it has inhabitants, they will return to the earth without trying to land.

Bolder spirits (including von Braun) are content with

no such half-measures. There is no sense, they say, in going to Mars unless they can land on it and shake hands or tentacles with a Martian welcoming committee. So von Braun and other equally ambitious astronauts have worked out in great detail just how to go to Mars, land upon it, leave it and return to the earth. They all admit that this enterprise will be a large one.

All their plans employ the basic method used by mountain climbers attacking a very high peak, such as Mount Everest. First a great troop of porters carries supplies and oxygen halfway up the mountain. They consume a good part of the food that they carry and must take another part of it for their homeward trip. A smaller number of porters carries the remainder farther up the mountain. A third group, even smaller, carries the diminishing stock a little way nearer the summit. Then the skilled mountain climbers (or the sponsors or financiers of the expedition) take the remaining supplies and oxygen and make their dash for glory. Each one of these star performers is using the combined endurance of many lesser men.

The same procedure will be followed in exploring Mars. First will come the familiar step of establishing a satellite on an orbit around the earth. This is equivalent to the first supply cache set up by the mountain-climbing porters. Then fueled and loaded space ships will take off from the satellite for the long journey to Mars. When they get there, they will establish a second supply cache in an orbit around it, reserving just enough fuel and supplies for their return trip.

After many such voyages, each of which will consume the payload of many rockets sent up from the earth, a second satellite station will be constructed in the Martian orbit.

The next step will be the landing on Mars. A special winged rocket will be constructed on the satellite out of parts brought over the long haul from the earth. The landing will be accomplished by atmospheric braking. Since the Martian atmosphere is thin, it will not offer as much support for the rocket's wings. On the other hand, Martian gravity is less than that of the earth, and much of Mars appears to be as flat and featureless as Texas. So a touchdown, say the astronauts, on a reddish Martian plain should not be too fast and dangerous.

Von Braun and his fellow planners do not consider, at this point, what will be the counteraction, if any, of the inhabitants of Mars. They plan to stay a short time, investigating interesting features that have been observed from the satellite. They will gather samples of Martial air and soil and examples of its flora and fauna, if they can find or catch any. They will then return to their friendly orbit, perhaps refueled for the voyage by a tanker rocket sent down from the satellite. When both Mars and the earth have reached favorable positions on their respective orbits, the explorers will start home to make their reports—and probably to describe their experiences on a world-wide television hook-up. They will have been away for more than three years; and they may not be in a mood for another interplanetary voyage.

A landing on Venus will be more difficult. The dense

atmosphere of Venus is always thick with clouds, and no one knows what lies below it. The surface may be totally dark, like the bottom of the ocean. So a landing will have to be accomplished by electronic guidance.

Voyages to the outer planets, such as Jupiter, Saturn and Neptune, are considerably more ambitious. These targets lie so far away that time begins to become a serious adversary. But as usual the astronauts have a ready answer. Instead of easing their space ships slowly from orbit to orbit, they propose to plunge downward past the sun and come out on the other side.

This "hyperbolic" course has certain disadvantages. A close approach to the sun looks a trifle risky, even to the hardiest astronaut, and before the sun can be approached, a great deal of fuel must be burned to cancel out the orbital velocity of a space ship that has started from the earth. The great advantage is saving of time. The space ship will drop toward the sun as a comet does and gain enormous speed. At its nearest approach to the sun's flaming surface, it will burn a large part of its remaining fuel. There is no point in carrying this burden up the other side of the sun's gravitational field. Thus lightened, the space ship will shoot outward to Jupiter or Saturn, where the space men no doubt will enjoy the coolness (close to absolute zero) of the outer planets.

All these projected voyages have numerous variants. One school of astronauts, centering in Britain, proposes to establish a permanent base on the moon. It will have the advantage (if it is an advantage) of moderate gravitation. There will be plenty of space for machine shops and observatories, and the moon's crust may prove to contain materials useful as supplies for the long voyages ahead. The moon is close enough to communicate easily with the earth. Its exiled inhabitants can enjoy earth-side television shows, although they will not be able to buy many of the products plugged by their commercials.

SPACE RADIO

The matter of communication in space has received a good deal of attention. It can be studied with precision on the earth, and the result of this examination is so encouraging that space-travel enthusiasts dwell on it lovingly. Even when their exaltation is strongest upon them, they like firm support under their feet, and the ease of radio communication is about the only item that they can be absolutely sure of.

An impressive analysis of space radio was recently made by George A. Smith of the Emerson Radio and Phonograph Corporation. The surface of the earth, Smith explained, is not favorable for radio communication. The air quickly absorbs much of the transmitter's energy, so the signals must pass in effect through a dense fog.

All sorts of electrical disturbances caused by man-made machinery get mixed up with the signal, reducing its intelligibility. Automobiles and aircraft contribute to this racket, as do diathermy units, welding apparatus, even electric bells and television sets. Another source of trouble is in the high atmosphere, where the sun stirs up a great variety of electrical uproar. Thunder-storms, which are always in progress somewhere on the earth, act as gigantic transmitting stations. Sometimes magnetic storms caused by electrified particles stream-ing out of the sun block out various types of radio com-munication.

In space all this local noise is absent, and the natural electrical noises of space are pleasantly mild. The sun sends out a certain amount of radio energy, and more of it comes from mysterious "dark stars." The center of the Milky Way galaxy whispers in radio signals like a gentle breeze stirring the needles of a pine grove. But all such noise is gentle compared to the racket on earth. On many of the most convenient wave lengths, the broadcasting stations of space are blissfully and abso-lutely silent.

The key factor with radio communication engineers is what they call the "signal-to-noise ratio." A radioed voice that has to compete with noise of equal strength cannot be understood at all. For good intelligibility, the voice should at least be ten times as strong as the noise that comes along with it. Even this strength is not sufficient if the noise comes in bursts, or if the voice signal is subject to fading. But the noise in space is as constant as the droning hum of a battery charger, and signals that pass through transparent space do not fade at all.

Smith wrote down the long equation which his colleagues use when figuring how much of a signal will reach its listeners and how much unavoidable noise will be received along with it. If both transmitter and receiver are in airless space, most of the noise-making factors drop out of the equation; so does the factor that represents the atmospheric absorption of radio waves; so does the factor that allows for the effect of signal fading. Almost nothing is left in the equation but the noise contributed by the transmitting and receiving apparatus. This is not serious.

Smith selects a three-centimeter wave as the most favorable frequency to use for space communication. When sent out through a dish-shaped antenna six feet in diameter, these waves form a narrow beam that spreads out in an angle of only one degree. The beam could be made narrower (thus concentrating its energy) by using shorter waves or a larger antenna, but Smith thinks that this gain would not be worth the extra effort. Seen from the earth, the moon is about half a degree across, so a one-degree beam blankets it nicely, allowing some margin for misaiming.

Targets more distant than the moon—Mars, for example—would be difficult to hit with a beam much narrower than one degree. Radio waves travel with the speed of light, but when Mars is at its nearest (35,000,-000 miles), they take three minutes to reach it. An answering signal sent back by a transmitter in the vicinity of Mars will take an equal time for the return journey.

During this six-minute period, the beam may have swung slightly because of the rapid motion of the space ship or satellite station on which its antenna is riding. The same will be true of the antenna near Mars. The man pointing the antenna will not know for at least six minutes whether his beam is hitting the target. If he depends on a very narrow beam, he may spend hours or days in futile groping through space. So Smith considers it prudent to use a fairly wide beam that will blanket Mars like a pattern of buckshot covering a considerable area around a flying duck. Then a message sent toward Mars will be reasonably sure of getting an answer in six minutes.

Having come to all these conclusions, Smith is now prepared to use his formula. He calculates that a six-foot antenna sending its beam of three-centimeter waves to a similar receiver on the moon can keep in clear voice communication using less than 3/10ths of a watt of electric current. This is less than the power demanded by an ordinary three-cell flashlight.

Clear conversation with Mars takes a great deal more power. Mars, at 35,000,000 miles, is 150 times as far away as the moon. Since the strength of a radio signal, even when traveling in a narrow beam, diminishes with the square of the distance, it will take 22,500 times as much power to talk with Mars as with the moon. This comes to about seven kilowatts, the power of a small broadcasting station, and admittedly difficult to generate on a space ship.

Smith is not discouraged by this temporary setback. Voice communication, he says, is pleasant and homey, but it takes a great deal more power than telegraphy. A teletype system works efficiently on 1/25th of the power of a voice system, so teletype communication with Mars will take only about 280 watts.

Even this moderate power requirement, less than half the power demanded by an electric toaster, can be cut by using tubes (magnetrons) that send out powerful pulses of energy and rest between them. Some magnetrons send out pulses 1,000 times as strong as the steady current that they consume. So a pulsed transmitter using less than one watt of current can work a teletype on Mars. This method makes it possible, Smith believes, to communicate handily with any part of the solar system.

The chief difficulty would be time, the enemy that dogs the steps of the more ambitious space travelers. Pluto, for instance, is never closer than three and one half billion miles from the earth. So a message to Pluto could not get its answer in less than ten hours. This is almost as bad as the old days on earth before the invention of the telegraph.

Only the more ambitious space travelers hope, however, to go to Pluto, which is not an attractive member of the solar system. The rest are immensely cheered by the comparative ease of radio communication among the nearer planets. With only a reasonable improvement on Smith's system, it might even be possible to set up a television station on Mars and invite Martian statesmen to participate electronically in the debates of the United Nations.

19

THE NEIGHBORS

When space-travel enthusiasts look at the sky, and not all of them do, they see only a few of the objects that they list as unfinished business on their agenda. The planets that they do see are not spectacular. Mercury looks like a medium faint star, always near the sun and therefore always dimmed by atmospheric haze just after sundown or just before dawn. Venus, Mars, Jupiter and Saturn are bright when nearby, but they are often far away on distant parts of their orbits. The other planets, Uranus, Neptune and Pluto, are not visible to the naked eye, and they were not discovered until telescopes were well developed. If the sky contained nothing but planets, it would look as bare as an empty room with only five birdshot scattered around as its furnishings.

Telescopes bring the planets closer. Venus looks like a hazy moon with no detail on its surface. It waxes and wanes as the moon does, and since it revolves in an orbit toward the sun, people on earth see only the dark side when Venus is nearest. Mars shows its full lighted face, but everyone who has seen it through a good telescope must have been disappointed. It looks like a small, jiggling ball, reddish brown in color and showing only faint and smoky markings. The great planets, Jupiter and Saturn, are glorious sights in a telescope, but it takes a hardy space-travel enthusiast to think of these distant and inhospitable worlds as favorable subjects for exploration or colonization.

When the space-minded enterpriser attempts to appraise the unimproved real estate floating near the earth, he is driven to the books of astronomers. What he finds in them is usually unsatisfactory. Most astronomers seem to feel that the planets are not worthy objects of their attention. They prefer to study the stars and the distant galaxies, whose light can be analyzed by spectroscopic methods and made to yield exact information almost as if it were data flowing out of the instruments of a laboratory experiment. Modern astronomers like to call themselves astrophysicists, and they shy away from the dim and dubious information that they can extract from the planets.

This snobbish attitude seems to be changing somewhat. Great telescopes are giving more of their time to planetary studies, and a few first-rate astronomers have become frankly interested in examining the planets from the point of view of their habitability. The information they seek cannot be obtained by mere looking, or by taking simple photographs. To get even a faint idea of what a planet is really like requires as elaborate and difficult methods as those that have been developed for the study of the stars.

When astronomers apply these methods, they come up against a non-scientific problem. Should they welcome or reject shreds of evidence that seem to make a planet hospitable to life? Their decision on this point should not be difficult; they should be able to judge such data as coldly as they would judge the evidence brought by a stellar spectrogram. But astronomers are human too. They fear the derision of their austere colleagues, and they know by sad experience that anything they may say about the habitability of a planet will be misquoted wildly by the lay press. Irresponsible space-fiction writers will misunderstand them, and elaborate their opinions into dozens of misleading stories. Then when the poor scientist goes to the next meeting of a professional society, he will be kidded unmercifully. So most astronomers stick to the stars, admittedly uninhabitable and therefore safer as objects for dignified theory-making.

When a competent astronomer does make a serious study of the planets, he usually surrounds his conclusions with mathematical equations that look like barbed-wire entanglements and have the same function: they keep outsiders away. Many space-fiction writers, for instance, must have tried to read astronomer Gerard

P. Kuiper's excellent book, *The Atmospheres of the Earth and the Planets*, but few of them can have penetrated beyond its outer defenses. Kuiper does not intend to be blamed for populating Venus with plants that look like beautiful women, but have chlorophyll in their skins.

Kuiper and his colleagues, however, have discovered a great deal about the planets in the last few years, and their special interest in planetary atmospheres is no scientific foible. As an environment for life of a reasonably familiar sort, a planet is only as good as its atmosphere. Without a gaseous cover to maintain pressure on the planet's surface, there can be no liquid water or other liquid, and without some liquid medium to promote its chemical reactions, life of the type known on earth is hardly conceivable.

The atmosphere of a planet is the product of a delicate balance of a great many physical forces. Chemical forces affect it too, and if life develops on the planet's surface, a powerful new kind of chemistry, biochemistry, comes into play.

The most striking property of all gases is that their molecules are in continuous rapid motion, each trying to get as far as possible from all the others. Unless restrained in some way, a gas expands until it fills any space available to it. The restraining force that keeps an atmosphere wrapped around a planet is, of course, the planet's gravitation. If the planet is large, its gravitation is strong and can hold an atmosphere more effectively. This is why small planetary bodies, such as asteroids, have no atmospheres at all. Their gravitation is too weak to keep free-flying gas molecules from shooting off into space.

Another physical factor is the planet's temperature. The hotter a gas becomes, the faster its molecules move. They struggle more effectively against restraining gravitation. Therefore a hot planet can retain less atmosphere than a cold planet of the same size.

Another factor is the size of the molecules in each individual gas. If the molecules are small, as in hydrogen or helium, they move more rapidly at a given temperature. Therefore they tend to escape more easily. If they are comparatively heavy, as in carbon dioxide, they move more slowly and therefore cannot escape as readily. So small, warm planets can retain only a few gases while large, cold planets can keep in their atmospheres the whole range of them, from hydrogen up to gases with very large molecules.

Armed with this information, the astronomers can predict with some accuracy whether a planet can have an atmosphere. They measure its mass and from it derive its gravitation. They estimate its surface temperature, which is roughly proportionate to its distance away from the sun. The combination of these two figures tells them what gases the planet can retain. But whether it actually has these gases depends on a great many other conditions.

The gases must come from some source, either the interior of the planet or outer space, and they must resist absorption by reactive materials on the planet's surface. Radiation from the sun has a destructive effect on a planet's atmosphere. It breaks the molecules of certain gases into smaller units that are able to escape into space. This is believed to have happened to a great deal of water vapor that once belonged to the earth. It was broken into hydrogen and oxygen. The hydrogen escaped, and the oxygen reacted with materials in the earth's crust. The same thing probably happened on other planets, notably Mars and perhaps Venus, both of which seem to have very little water left.

When astronomers try to study directly the atmospheres that exist on the planets at present, they do not have much success. Mercury and the moon have no detectable atmospheres. In the case of Venus, all that the astronomers can see is a white, shining, featureless cloud deck. Jupiter has a cloud deck too, which shows markings that suggest a continuous procession of violent storms. Saturn, Uranus, Neptune and Pluto are too far away to allow their atmospheres to be studied with any kind of accuracy. Only Mars has an atmosphere that is transparent enough to be examined down to its bottom.

Sunlight reflected from a planetary cloud deck brings little information. When examined spectroscopically it shows the familiar solar spectrum, somewhat dimmed and fuzzed up. The most interesting items are dark bands that show that the sunlight has penetrated a little way into the planet's atmosphere and has been reflected out again after certain wave lengths have been partially absorbed by gases in the planet's atmosphere. Theoretically these bands should tell what gases the atmosphere contains, but in practice they speak only in the faintest whispers. Some gases, such as nitrogen, do not absorb wave lengths that man's instruments can detect. Other gases contribute sharply defined absorption bands, but the meaning of these is obscured by absorption caused by the same gases in the earth's atmosphere. In some cases the two absorption effects can be separated by extremely delicate techniques, but the information gained in this way is dubious, to put it mildly.

Such meager information from the top of a planetary cloud deck does not tell much about the atmosphere that lies beneath it. The structure of the earth's atmosphere, the only one that man knows well, is extremely complicated. At the surface it may be either hot or cold, according to latitude, season or nature of the surface below. A little farther up it is always cold. Then it gets hot again. The temperature drops and rises at least once more before the last layers fray out into space. Thick planetary atmospheres are probably just as complicated and may be more so, but none of their details can be studied by examining their cloud decks.

Those few astronomers who have condescended to study the cloud-covered planets with the most modern techniques have not yet come to many firm conclusions. They think, for instance, that the atmosphere of Venus is extremely deep, but they are not too sure about it. They think it contains carbon dioxide, but they do not know how much. They do not know what its clouds are made of.

The atmospheres of Jupiter and Saturn are believed

to contain methane and ammonia, but that is about all that the astronomers are sure of. The enormous reddish spot that seems to be a permanent feature of the Jovian atmosphere is a complete mystery. No theory to explain it is convincing at all.

The surfaces of the cloud-covered planets are utterly unknown. Venus may have a deep ocean, perhaps of water, perhaps of some other liquid such as liquid carbon dioxide. It may be dry and covered with some kind of fine dust, which is raised into the atmosphere by winds to form the conspicuous white clouds. It may be hot, it may be cold. It may have high mountains on it; it may be smooth. No one knows. If the atmosphere is as thick and opaque as most astronomers think it is, the surface of Venus is probably as dark as the bottom of the earth's ocean.

The surface of Jupiter is probably thousands of miles below the top of its atmosphere, and pressure upon it must be enormous. Below the highly compressed gases may be many thousand miles of liquids of some sort. Jupiter is so large that its interior must give off a great deal of heat. So its oceans may be boiling violently from volcanic eruptions. The storms that seem to break through the top of the Jovian atmosphere may be proof that tremendous turmoil is continuous below.

The key fact about Mercury, the innermost planet, is that it always turns the same side toward the sun. The sun-facing side must be hot enough to melt many metals, and the side that faces away from the sun is probably one of the coldest places in the solar system.

It gets no warmth except from the stars and from an occasional planet passing nearby. So its temperature must be close to absolute zero. Mercury can have no real atmosphere. It is too hot and too small to retain one permanently. The cold side may be covered, however, with frozen gases which are as solid at the prevailing temperature as if they were layers of rock.

Around the middle of Mercury there must be a belt that gets only slanting sunlight. Some optimistic space men have imagined that this zone may be a kind of paradise with a temperature, climate and other conditions favorable to the development of life. Astronomers do not agree with this cheery opinion. There can be no atmosphere over this "paradise zone." If there were, its gases would immediately shoot out into space or move to the cold side of the planet to condense into rock. There can be no water or other liquids. Any object that pokes up into the fierce blast of nearly horizontal sunlight will be heated at once to an impossible temperature, and any object in a shadow will cool quickly to the neighborhood of absolute zero. These are not conditions that are friendly to life.

The best-known object in space is the earth's own moon. It is less than a quarter-million miles away, a mere step in the solar system, and its lack of an atmosphere allows its surface to be studied in sharp detail. A great tribe of astronomers—most of them dedicated amateurs—stare at the moon at every favorable moment. They memorize its mysterious markings and get to know them as well as gardeners know their flower beds.

A vast amount of detailed literature has been accumulating for more than a hundred years about the surface markings of the moon. The most surprising thing to an outside observer is the almost complete lack of agreement among the lunar experts. Some of them see the moon's great ring-shaped craters, its most striking feature, as results of volcanic activity. Others claim that they are scars made by meteorites. Some believe that the moon's plains are covered with lava extruded from the interior. Others say that they are the healed scars of meteoric impacts when the moon was young. According to this theory, planetoids many miles in diameter hit the moon long ago and were melted by the energy of their impact. The fused material spread slowly over the moon's surface, obliterating mountains and other features that it found in its path.

When modern astronomical instruments are turned upon the moon, they do not bring back a great deal of new information. The moon's surface is apparently covered in level places with a fine grayish dust which reflects light in about the same way as certain earthside materials. The depth of this dust is unknown, though there are theories about it. The rocky materials of the moon are presumed to be much like earthly rocks, although one theory holds that there is a good deal of metal around: nickel and iron contributed by meteorites.

Some students of the moon believe that volcanic activity stopped many million years ago. Others see faint signs that it still continues, claiming that certain markings have changed in the last few years. They insist that they have seen small, short-lived clouds on the moon, and these they attribute to gases issuing out of crevices.

Most astronomers agree that the moon has no atmosphere, except perhaps a few hydrogen atoms recently arrived from the hydrogen-spitting sun and revolving around it on orbits of their own. A minority claims that this atmosphere is dense enough to be important. Since the earth is bombarded by meteors, they point out, the moon should be bombarded just as heavily. If the moon has no atmosphere to slow meteors down, their impacts against its dark face should give flashes of light bright enough to be seen in man's telescopes. A few astronomers claim to have seen such flashes, but most of the moon-gazers who stare at the moon for years of nights have seen nothing of the sort.

One explanation of the lack of meteor flashes is that the moon's atmosphere, too thin to be detected in any other way, may still be dense enough to slow the incoming meteors. Since the braking effect is very gradual, they do not get hot enough to show streaks of light as they do when they hit the earth. When they finally arrive at the moon's surface, they do not hit it hard enough to give bright flashes. This theory, which is not supported by many, is cheering to the space men. If the moon's thin atmosphere can slow down meteors, it can also slow a properly designed space ship and allow it to land on the moon without a damaging impact.

Only the most fanatical devotees of the moon profess to see life upon it. They admit that most of its unchanging surface is as lifeless as cooling slag, but they fasten their eyes and their hopes on a few small crevices that seem to change color during the long lunar day, which lasts fourteen earth days. During the lunar night, according to this theory, the crevices fill with carbon dioxide escaping from the moon's interior. It is cold enough to hang around for a while, and as the sun rises very slowly over the gas-filled lunar valley, primitive plants grow feebly on the lunar rocks. They must be very peculiar plants which can resist the ferocious heat of the lunar midday and the equally terrible cold of the lunar night, but optimistic space men plan to harvest them and to use them for what they are worth.

20

FRUITFUL MARS

Mars is the most satisfactory planet. It comes close enough to the earth to be studied in some detail. Its atmosphere is dense enough to make some sort of life possible, and it is not so dense and opaque that it hides the surface completely, as does the atmosphere of Venus.

Mars is much smaller than the earth. It has a little more than half the earth's diameter and about one-tenth of the earth's mass, but it resembles the earth in ways that make its would-be explorers feel rather at home. Its day is a little longer than an earthside day (24 hours, 37 minutes, $22\frac{1}{2}$ seconds), and brilliant white ice caps form on its poles, much as they do on the earth's. The surface of Mars changes with the seasons in a way that suggests strongly the growth of vegetation.

In the days before the development of spoil sport astronomy, it was widely believed that the moon was inhabited by people not very different from people on earth. Less than one hundred years ago it was still possible for hoaxing newspapers to convince their readers that astronomers had discovered beautiful cities on the moon, with fertile fields around them and a marvelous civilization. This pleasant fantasy faded away as knowledge of the moon's austerity reached the popular mind.

But the wise and beautiful inhabitants of the moon did not die entirely; they merely moved to Mars, which cannot be studied accurately enough to disprove their existence. The Martians who live so persistently in space fiction are a product of this uncertainty. No one can prove conclusively that they do not exist, and the vague information that trickles down from Mars suggests to the hopeful that perhaps they do.

Mars had a kind of Florida boom in the late nineteenth century when the Italian astronomer Schiaparelli claimed to have seen on it some straight, regular bands that he named canals. The boom gained real headway when the wealthy American astronomer Percival Lowell (brother of the cigar-smoking poetess, Amy Lowell, and of Abbott Lawrence Lowell, the sedate president of Harvard) set up a large telescope in the clear air of Flagstaff, Arizona, and proceeded to clothe Mars with a civilization far in advance of anything known on earth.

Each time Mars swung near the earth on its orbit, Lowell saw more canals: fine dark lines crisscrossing the face of the small red planet like a geometrical spider-web. Some of them were double and exactly parallel. Where they crossed there were often broad patches of dark surface. The canals changed with the Martian seasons, propagating from the poles as if some mysterious influence were moving along them. On these observations, Lowell built a wonderful theory of Martian cultural history, and his enthusiastic followers embroidered it ecstatically.

Mars is older than the earth, said Lowell. That is, its small size made it pass through all of its stages sooner than the earth did. Life developed sooner and became intelligent sooner. The generally smooth surface of Mars indicates that it once had oceans on it. Life evolved in the Martian oceans and moved to the Martian continents. At this point, many million years ago, Mars resembled the earth today, with intelligent beings of some sort leading the life of Martian Riley on well-watered, fertile lands.

Then the slow, inexorable laws of planetary physics began to catch up with the Martians. Molecules of water vapor that diffused the top of their atmosphere were broken by sunlight into oxygen and hydrogen. The hydrogen escaped from the weak Martian gravitation (about two-fifths as strong as the earth's), and the oxygen was absorbed by iron compounds in the surface rocks. This explains the reddish color of Mars, for highly oxidized iron is generally red.

While this was happening, volcanic activity gradually died down. The flow of gases and water vapor from the planet's interior became less and less. Deprived of re placements, the atmosphere of Mars grew thin. Its oceans evaporated, leaving great red deserts that were once their floors.

This process of desiccation, said Lowell, was gradual, taking millions of years. By the time the situation be came serious, the Martians had reached a degree of intelligence that permitted them to do something about it. They could not keep the water of their planet from moving out into space, but they could make the best use of what little remained.

The Martian polar regions act like those of the earth. They are great condensers that gather water vapor from the atmosphere and lock it to the surface as snow or ice. When one of the Martian poles turns toward the sun during the spring of its hemisphere, the ice melts as it does on earth. The Martians, said Lowell, took advantage of this circumstance. They dug great canals to gather the water of the melting polar caps and lead it toward the Martian equator to irrigate dried-up lands. Lowell did not explain why the canals appear straight. On earth, irrigation canals always curve around the contours, however slight they may be. But presumably the highly intelligent Martians had some good reason for making their canals straight.

Present-day Mars, said Lowell, is a dying planet which is kept from lifelessness only by the high intelligence of its inhabitants. The canals visible to observers on earth are broad belts of lush vegetation irrigated by water running down channels in their middles. At their intersections are larger oases which are presumably the major centers of Martian cultural life. Each half-year, as the ice melts on one pole of the desert planet, a Mars-wide irrigation commission opens the sluice-gates and starts a great system of pumps. Water courses down the canals, bringing new life to the fields beside them, just as the annual flood of the Nile brings life to Egypt. Then half a Martian year later, the ice cap on the opposite pole yields another gush of water.

On this theory of Lowell's has been built a marvelous structure of Martian lore. If life on Mars reached the intelligent stage fifty or one hundred million years ago, it must be much more intelligent now. The Martians must have developed enormously effective brains. Perhaps they can control their bodies and shape them to their own desires.

They must have discovered secrets of nature still hidden from human minds. Perhaps they can communicate by mental telepathy. Perhaps they have made themselves immaterial and invisible, retaining the essence of life while divorcing themselves from material needs. Perhaps even the canal system is a relic of past Martian ages. The present inhabitants may be bodiless ghosts that live on a higher plane of existence compounded of thought and emotion. Perhaps when the earth's explorers land on the plains of Mars, they will pass right through the Martians, without realizing that they are there.

According to these self-deprecatory theorists, the crude invaders from the young rough earth will seem to the Martians as primitive as dinosaurs. Perhaps they will greet them with the qualified friendliness of scientists welcoming experimental animals into their laboratories. Perhaps they will destroy them with a single sharp flick of some unimaginable weapon. Or perhaps they will be amused to watch the earthlings colonizing their planet, wholly unaware that it already has a well-established population.

These conjectures about ancient, civilized Mars and the wise old race that inhabits it depend almost entirely on the observations and theories of Percival Lowell. There is no doubt about Lowell's competence as an astronomer. His mathematical calculations were responsible, among other things, for the discovery of the planet Pluto. But Lowell's temperament seems to have resembled that of his poet sister more than that of his staid, Harvard-president brother. He let his imagination overpower his scientific judgment.

When other astronomers look at Mars, they see nothing resembling Lowell's canals and oases. A few see fine lines, but they are not arranged in the same pattern as Lowell's. Photographs do not help at all. Even when taken with the finest instruments under the best circumstances, they show only hazy blotches rather like a map of the earth seen dimly through frosted glass.

For more than seventy years astronomers have argued about what can or cannot be seen on Mars, and unscholarly epithets have echoed in dignified seminars. The fierceness and persistence of this long-lived controversy is hard for laymen to understand. To them it seems

simple to look at Mars with a good telescope and decide
once and for all what can be seen upon it. It is not as
easy as that.

Laymen are so much impressed by large telescopes
that they can hardly believe they have limitations. The
200-inch telescope on Palomar Mountain looks as if it
could drag Mars out of the sky and cut it up into California real estate. It can do no such thing. The Palomar
telescope was designed for a specific purpose: to inten-
sify the light from distant stars and galaxies and make
it strong enough to be analyzed by the battery of new
instruments developed by the astrophysicists. This job
it does very successfully, but for observing small details
on Mars it is no better than much less ambitious instruments.

Telescopes have many failings. The worst one is
caused by the earth's turbulent atmosphere, whose irregularities act like the "heat waves" that distort objects
on the horizon during a hot day. They make the stars
and planets jiggle around, and the more they are magnified the more they jiggle. When the light from a star
is to be analyzed by a spectroscope or measured by a
photo cell, this jiggling does not do much harm, but it
makes fine details on the face of a planet as difficult to
see as the print on a fluttering newspaper.

Most astronomical observation is now done by means
of photography. The telescope is a great camera that is
kept pointing accurately in the same direction for several hours or even for several nights. Faint light from
distant parts of the universe gradually builds an impres-

sion on the photographic plate. The vision of the plate is cumulative, so the plate can see distant objects that are much too faint for the human eye. But the image formed on the plate during a long exposure is made slightly fuzzy by the continuous trembling due to atmospheric turbulence. Stars show as small "disks of confusion," and fine details on the surface of a planet disappear entirely.

The human eye works differently. It cannot build up an image; prolonged staring will not make it see objects that are too faint to affect its retina. But the eye is much quicker than the plate. Sometimes it catches fine details before they have a chance to move.

This is why direct visual observation, which is considered obsolete for most kinds of astronomy, is still the best way to observe the planets. The astronomer waits for a favorable "presentation" when the planet that he is studying is closest to the earth. Then with a sketch pad handy, he watches the blurred, jiggling globe in his telescope's field of vision. Most of the time he sees nothing particularly interesting, only the general outlines about which he and his colleagues agree. At wide intervals, if he is lucky, he gets short instants of perfect seeing. The atmosphere above his telescope happens to be smooth, or the effects of several irregularities happen to cancel out. Then his eye catches a fleeting glimpse of a wealth of detail on the face of the planet. He sketches furiously, trying to record the momentary vision.

When the astronomer has done this many times, perhaps for a lifetime of intermittent observing, he builds up his version of what the planet really looks like. The result is sure to be affected by his personal temperament. If he is cautious, he puts down only those markings that he has seen frequently in the same places. If he is less cautious, he sketches things that he saw only once. If he yields to wishful seeing (and astronomers are not less human than other men), he sketches details that he thought he saw—which are really parts of a pattern which he has formed in his mind.

Conservative students of Mars accuse Lowell and his followers of doing just this. They say that the whole theory of the Martian canals and the wonderful people who designed them grew out of the accident of Schiaparelli's choice of words. He saw faint straight lines on Mars and called them *canali*, which means "channels" in Italian. Lowell and his followers turned the *canali* into irrigation canals and built upon them their gaudy conception of Martian civilization. Then, of course, when they looked at Mars, they saw oases and seasonal changes that tended to support their theory of the Martian irrigation system.

Actually it is possible to see or not see almost anything on Mars. Observed through a good telescope when it is near the earth, Mars looks about like the moon seen with the naked eye as it rises through the heat waves above a sun-warmed pavement. Its image shimmers and trembles, and the straining eye sees tantalizing details appearing and disappearing on it. Sometimes for a brief instant the whole face of the planet looks wonderfully clear.

Unfortunately, the human system of visual recording is not designed to take in a large amount of detail in a half-second or less. So the too short intervals of clairvoyance leave the frustrated astronomer feeling that he has dreamed a vivid, detailed dream that he cannot remember properly. It is no wonder that many sincere and honest astronomers have made sketch maps of Mars that do not match in any respect what their colleagues have seen.

The possibility of space flight has stimulated interest in Mars, and many astronomers are trying to develop methods of studying it that are better than visual observation. One possibility is to take motion pictures of Mars during its next near approach in 1956. The Palomar telescope, which gathers four times as much light as its nearest rival, is the only instrument that can do this effectively. Using the most sensitive photographic film, it can probably take pictures of Mars in about one-fiftieth of a second. This is approximately as fast as the human eye works. If a movie is taken of Mars during an entire night of exceptionally good seeing, one or more of the frames, each exposed for only one-fiftieth of a second, may show the planet unblurred by atmospheric turbulence. Such a picture will be free of the artifacts of human imagination. It will be permanent and can be analyzed, grain by grain, using the careful microscopic techniques well known to astronomers.

Perhaps it will show a planet elaborately organized by an intelligent race. Perhaps it will show only lifeless details like those on the lifeless moon. No one knows at present, and no one is sure that the trick will work.

Mars can be studied in other ways than by observing its surface detail, and this is being done with some success. Modern photoelectric cells, which measure temperatures accurately, have brought a good deal of information about the climate of Mars. It is not good from the human point of view, but ñot impossible.

During the middle of the day, the temperature of the ground near the Martian equator is believed to rise as high as seventy or eighty degrees Fahrenheit. At night it falls far below zero Fahrenheit. In regions nearer the poles it is colder, and in winter it stays below zero during both night and day. Mars may be said to have a continental climate, something like the Gobi Desert, but even more violent in its temperature changes.

Careful astronomers are quick to add, however, that they are not at all sure about these figures. They can estimate them only by measuring the heat that comes from sections of the Martian disk. This is a delicate operation, and its validity is doubtful because the astronomers do not know what the surface of Mars is made of. They do not know much about the atmosphere either, and they fear that on some occasions they may have measured the temperature of clouds hanging high above the surface.

Astronomers agree that it never rains on Mars. The atmosphere is too thin to supply the conditions that bring rain on earth. The nearest thing to Martian rain is the condensation of moisture on the polar caps, where a thin layer of snow or ice or hoar frost is deposited every winter. When spring comes to an ice-covered polar zone, the water crystals melt. What happens next is under vigorous and sometimes ill-tempered debate—like almost every other phenomenon on Mars.

As an ice cap disappears with the coming of spring, a dark band forms along the edge of its glittering whiteness. Simultaneously an "influence" of some sort spreads slowly and irregularly toward the equator. Patches on the surface turn from light greenish-gray to dark brown. The advancing dark region has an irregular edge, and the irregularities are always in the same places. Some areas do not change color, and these seem permanent too. The color change advances toward the equator at an average speed of about eleven miles per day, but in places it moves much faster.

No one seriously believes that the darkness moving toward the equator is caused by a great flood of water released from the polar caps. The caps are too thin to supply sufficient water, and there is no force available to make water flow in such a manner. The most widely accepted hypothesis is that when the ice melts it saturates the soil directly beneath it, thus forming the dark band. All soils made of mineral particles look darker when wet than when dry.

Liquid water cannot exist on Mars except just above its freezing point; atmospheric pressure is so low that water evaporates quickly if it gets much warmer. So soon after the ice cap melts, the water produced is believed to evaporate. Then it is carried by slow winds toward the Martian equator. As the moist air moves, it favors the growth of vegetation that has been dormant during the dry, cold winter. This is believed to account for the change of color.

Martian vegetation cannot be like any plants on earth; the dark areas do not reflect light as chlorophyll does. But this is not proof that plant life does not exist upon them. Many earthly plants, including the brown and red seaweeds, get along fine with no green chlorophyll.

In fact, the Martian vegetation would have to be different, because it must live under different conditions. The atmosphere of Mars is believed to contain carbon dioxide, but no trace of oxygen has been found in it. Most earthside plants absorb carbon dioxide when exposed to sunlight and give off oxygen, but they die in an atmosphere that has no oxygen at all. Earthside animals, of course, need an atmosphere to supply them with large amounts of oxygen. So the Martian atmosphere, at first glance, does not look hospitable to life.

Present knowledge of the Martian atmosphere, however, is not detailed enough to support any firm conclusions. There may be oxygen in sufficient quantity to support some kind of animal life. There may be other gases, such as hydrogen sulphide, that play their parts in an other-worldly metabolism. Astronomers do not know.

They know very little, in fact, about the atmosphere of Mars. They can see that it contains several kinds of clouds. Some of them are white and always near the surface. They may be made of floating ice crystals like the cirrus clouds in the higher levels of the earth's atmosphere. There are also large yellow clouds that move around the Martian surface, sometimes for several months, two or three miles above the ground. These have been supposed to be clouds of dust, and space-fiction writers have adopted them as permanent and proved features of life on Mars. Astronomers are not so sure. The winds on Mars are not very powerful, moving only a few miles per hour, and it is difficult to see how their feeble force could support much dust for months in the thin Martian air.

Above the yellow clouds is a violet haze which sometimes covers the whole face of the planet, obscuring details beneath it. This is a total mystery, and so are the blue clouds that float above it, as much as nineteen miles above the surface. Astronomers have not the faintest idea about what they are made of.

Most of them agree that there is something extraordinary, and extraordinarily interesting, on the planet Mars. It is presumably as old as the earth, and there is good reason to believe that it once had more water on it. Its surface is generally very smooth, and without the eroding action of water it would probably be as jagged as the surface of the moon.

If there were once oceans on Mars, life could develop in them just as it did on earth. It could do so even if the oceans were a great deal smaller and shallower. Life on earth developed in the ocean's surfaces, where the sun penetrates.

Since life on Mars would presumably be as resourceful as it is on earth, it could probably adapt itself to gradually worsening conditions. The departure of the oxygen and most of the water vapor from the Martian atmosphere might not be a killing handicap. There are low forms of life on earth that live without oxygen and do very well. Among them are the familiar yeasts which "breathe" sugar and "breathe out" alcohol. Other types have strange metabolisms that get energy from hydrogen sulfide or iron compounds.

If life on earth can adapt to such odd conditions, it is not too much to expect that life on Mars might learn to get along in an atmosphere without oxygen, even without dependence on any atmosphere. It might, for instance, enclose its living tissues in virtually gas-tight membranes. This would not be very different from the system of earthside plants and land animals that live in desert climates. The active material in their cells consists of substances dissolved in water, but they have no trouble living where water is obtainable only with great difficulty. One further step may have been taken by the Martian plants: that of conserving oxygen as well as water and storing it in their tissues, either as a gas or as some chemical compound rich in oxygen.

If such plants exist on Mars, there is an obvious opening for animals that prey upon them. If the plants contain both oxygen and carbon compounds, the animal that eats them will be eating and breathing too.

Astronomers generally leave such speculation to the space-fiction writers, who are seldom equipped with enough knowledge to make their speculations reasonable. Most of them have peopled Mars with intelligent beings adapted in only one or two ways to the special conditions of the Martian environment. They imagine them with very large lungs to breathe the thin Martian air, and cover them with dense woolly coats to ward off the Martian cold. This is not enough adaptation to permit survival.

If intelligent beings do exist on Mars, they are certainly not at all like the *dramatis personae* of space fiction. They are just as likely to be disembodied brains like those coldly intelligent creatures that descended on the earth in H. G. Wells's *War of the Worlds*. They may even be clever fungi with sedentary central intelligences directing the operations of far-reaching food-gathering organs. Not enough is known about Mars to give even the sketchiest idea of what its inhabitants are like and how they live—or whether they exist at all above the level of lichens or algae.

21

OTHER-WORLDLY LIFE

There is a curious blank in the scientific literature of space. So far as this observer knows, there is no full-scale, responsible and informed study of the kinds of life that might develop under circumstances different from those on earth. Plenty of amateurs have speculated wildly about it. They imagine planets with atmospheres of corrosive fluorine; they even describe in some detail the inhabitants of the sun, which is too hot for any chemical compound and which consists entirely of gases stirred by ferocious turbulence. But no fully competent scientist has made a serious attack on this interesting subject.

One reason may be that scientists have an inordinate respect for the jurisdictional boundaries between their specialties. A biologist feels like a prowler in the night when he ventures into psychology. Astronomers dive for their cyclone cellars when the conversation veers even slightly toward biology. Some sciences have become so finely subdivided that specialists in closely related fields hardly speak to one another. A protein chemist has little to say to a steroid chemist. Both may be trying to find a chemical cure for cancer, but neither would dream of commenting on the other's problems.

To write a successful book on the possibilities of extra-terrestrial life would require good knowledge in many widely separated fields. The author would have to be a broad biologist, familiar with all the forms that have been explored by life on earth. He would have to know organic chemistry, which is concerned with carbon com-pounds, and also inorganic chemistry. He would have to know the many kinds of physics that deal with condi-tions in the atmospheres, the oceans and on the surfaces of other planets than the earth. He would have to know enough about astronomy to read the extremely difficult literature that professional astronomers circulate in their small, charmed circle.

Such a man does not exist, or if he does exist, he has kept his talents unknown to the general public. The subject of extraterrestrial life has been abandoned to the space-fiction writers, who usually imagine lovely girls with yellow eyes, antennae growing out of their fore-heads and lungs full of fluorine. This is a crying shame. Life is the most interesting thing in the entire universe; it deserves better treatment.

The study of life in general starts with a strange blank. No one has succeeded in defining what life is. J. B. S. Haldane has called it "any self-perpetuating pattern of chemical reactions," but this is too inclusive to suit all of his colleagues. A flame, for instance, is chemical and self-perpetuating. It consumes fuel and oxygen and breathes out carbon dioxide just like the animals on earth. It "lives" as long as it can find both fuel and oxygen. It dies when one of them is exhausted, just as animals die of starvation or suffocation. But a flame is not alive in the sense of the biologist. It is not a living organism.

When biologists try to point to the simplest possible organisms, they run into difficulties too. Certain viruses, such as those that cause the mosaic disease of tobacco, behave from the point of view of the tobacco grower just like any other pathogenic organism. They infect his tobacco plants, grow inside them and spread to other plants throughout his field. But when the apparently living virus is isolated, it proves to be nothing but a large molecule. It forms regular crystals much like those of common salt and behaves in many other ways like a lifeless chemical compound.

To decide whether tobacco mosaic is really a living organism is a problem in semantics. To call it lifeless is dangerous. It certainly multiplies and replenishes the earth within its small field, just like the fruitful people of the Old Testament. To call it alive is dangerous too. When packed together in a crystal, its molecules show no signs of life. It is then a mere chemical compound, and although it is very complicated it might presumably be synthesized in the scientists' glassware. Then the scientists would have created life. Or wouldn't they?

For the present at least, the scientists have abandoned this problem of definition to the semanticists and philosophers, tribes for which they have little respect. A living organism, they say in effect, is anything that grows, reproduces, and perpetuates itself or its species. It needs some source of energy for this operation and it must have the ability to absorb substances of which to build its bodily mechanism. The energy can come from any available source and so can building materials.

When scientists try to figure out how life got started on earth, they are forced into many assumptions that they cannot prove. The simplest organisms to be found on earth today—the viruses—are parasitic. They do not live independently, but prey on higher organisms. The tobacco virus for instance can live and grow only within the cells of the tobacco plant, and other viruses are restricted in the same way. Obviously, they cannot be the original forms of life, which must have lived independently before higher organisms developed.

Most of the bacteria, one step upward, are parasitic too. They live by digesting the organic materials elaborated by higher creatures. Even those few that live independently cannot be the original forms of life on earth; they are too highly developed.

A bacterium looks simple in the field of a microscope, but it is extremely complicated, both chemically and in its interior structure. It cannot have sprung full grown, like Athena from the forehead of Zeus, out of the inorganic chemicals in the lifeless, primitive earth. There must have been simpler organisms, now extinct, from which all higher forms evolved in the course of time. When the scientists make the assumption that such organisms existed, their task becomes simpler. They can give them any properties that seem to make sense.

At present the energy source of all, or nearly all, life on earth is the light of the sun. It is absorbed by chlorophyll and similar compounds in the cells of plants and is used to combine water and carbon dioxide to form sugars and other organic compounds that the plant needs for its growth. This is an extremely complicated operation, and most of the experts on this subject believe that the earliest organisms must have got along without it.

They picture the early earth as very different from the earth today. Its atmosphere contained many carbon compounds, such as the methane that can still be detected in the atmospheres of the outer planets. Carbon has the property of combining with itself to form large, complicated, "organic" molecules. Under the influence of sunlight and perhaps of cosmic rays, much of the methane in the early atmosphere combined into these large molecules and washed down into the sea. There the molecules grew larger by combining with one another and with other substances such as nitrogen, sulphur, phosphorus, iron, magnesium, oxygen and hydrogen.

This process continued slowly for hundreds of millions of years until the sea was full of a kind of organic soup. It probably contained examples of all the compounds that carbon will form with the other available elements. This stuff does not exist in the sea today; it could not exist because living organisms would attack it and destroy it immediately, but in the primitive sea there was no life. So the organic molecules could grow indefinitely.

At last the blind process of chemical combination, repeated hundreds of trillions of times in each microsecond, produced a molecule with an extraordinary property. It could grow by taking other molecules into its structure, and it could reproduce, probably by the simple maneuver of breaking in two. This molecule was "alive," and a new and powerful force had appeared on the earth.

Feeding on the lifeless foodstuffs dissolved in the water, the descendants of the Adam-and-Eve molecule quickly populated all the primitive oceans. Some of them changed slightly so that they could utilize more of the available foodstuffs. Some of them became fierce molecular predators feeding on weaker fellows. How long this primitive kind of life had the earth to itself the scientists do not attempt to guess. It may have been several hundred million years, for the earth is four billion years old at least, and its surface has had a tolerable temperature for nearly as long.

Once life appeared, it was forced by its very nature to become more complicated. The simplest living molecules could not exploit all the possible modes of life available at the time, so when more complicated forms were created by chemical or physical accidents, they had an advantage over their more primitive relatives. They grew and multiplied faster, only to be replaced in turn by still more complicated forms. At last organisms appeared that did not depend on the carbon compounds dissolved in the ocean. They made their own by photosynthesis out of carbon dioxide and light.

This was a second great turning point. Now life was hitched to the unfailing power of the shining sun. The primitive photosynthetic organisms may have been red or purple or any other color, but they were real plants. They were so successful that they soon cleaned the carbon dioxide out of the atmosphere, replacing it with the oxygen that dominates it chemically today. Soon primitive parasites (animals) developed to devour the plants. These breathed oxygen and breathed out carbon dioxide, which flowed back to the plants.

Thus was established the celebrated carbon cycle. Plants dominate the earth today in a chemical sense, keeping the carbon dioxide in its atmosphere down to a mere trace. The animals and the parasitic bacteria and fungi try to keep up with the plants, returning the carbon to the atmosphere where it can be used again to build more plants. Once life had been established on this firm basis, the rest of evolution was only a matter of time. It probably took less than a billion years for evolution to produce the intelligent animal, man, that now dominates the planet.

Scientists point out that there is nothing miraculous or unrepeatable about the appearance of life on earth.

They believe it would happen again, given the same sufficient time and the same set of circumstances. It would even happen under very different circumstances. There is no reason to believe that conditions in the atmosphere and oceans of the primitive earth were modified by any outside power to make them favorable for the development of life. They just happened that way, and it is likely that life woud have appeared even if conditions had been considerably different.

Not very much skilled reasoning has been applied to the problem of what conditions are absolutely necessary for the appearance of life. Conservative theorists hold that life must be based on carbon compounds like those that form human and other living bodies. They claim that only carbon can join in the long chains, complicated rings, and other molecular patterns that are needed to make the life process work.

If this is true, the climate must be just right. At very low temperatures, carbon compounds do not react readily with one another, and at the temperature of boiling water many of them disintegrate. Another limitation insisted upon by the conservative theorists is that life must have large amounts of water. Complicated carbon compounds will dissolve in other liquids than water, but not as well and not in the same way. Besides liquid water, there must be a supply of simple carbon compounds in the early stages, and this rules out environments rich in chemical substances (such as free oxygen) that would destroy them. Another necessity is light, which is the activating agent that induces small molecules to combine into larger ones.

Less conservative theorists claim that the conditions demanded by the conservatives may be necessary for the production of life as it is known on earth. But other kinds of life, they say, may be possible, and they may demand or tolerate very different conditions. The chemistry of carbon has been studied more intensively than that of any other element, but the limits of its possibilities have not been approached. There may be carbon compounds that will react vigorously even when dissolved in some novel medium, such as liquid ammonia. There may be others that will tolerate extremely high temperatures.

Living organisms on earth have not had to synthesize such carbon compounds, and human chemists have not tried very hard to do so. When they do try, they sometimes have rather surprising success. Synthetic rubber, which is made of typical organic carbon compounds, is now being formed deliberately at very low temperatures, and it turns out to be better than rubber made at high temperatures.

At the other end of the temperature scale, the silicones (compounds containing both carbon and silicon) have proved to be stable far above the boiling point of water. There seems to be an unlimited number of possible silicones, so a planet with a very dense atmosphere and an ocean of water above the normal boiling point of water on earth might possibly develop living organisms with bodies made of silicones. Some chemists think that this is impossible, but at the present state of their knowledge they cannot prove it.

Neither can they prove that life is impossible in a medium other than water. They know little about the chemistry of complicated substances dissolved, say, in liquid hydrocarbons at a very low temperature. Their reactions might be slow, but the universe has plenty of time at its disposal. No one can prove, for instance, that Jupiter does not have a cold hydrocarbon ocean, or that it does not contain a slow sort of life.

It is even possible, theoretically, that life can develop in a gaseous instead of a liquid medium. A theory advanced seriously by Dr. Heinz Haber of the University of California at Los Angeles suggests that the mysterious clouds in the atmosphere of Venus may be a "biological airsol," a fog of small living organisms supported at the most favorable altitude in respect to sunlight and temperature. They would be like the plankton that forms the bulk of life in the earth's oceans, and larger flying organisms may have developed to feed upon them, like the earth's fish. Perhaps the bodies of all these creatures rain down eventually to the surface of Venus, which is probably dark and may be rather hot. If not too hot, it may be populated by large scavenging animals that live on the nutritious rain, just like the crabs and mollusks on the bottoms of the earth's oceans.

Once life gets started, it seems to have an unlimited ability to fit itself to changing conditions. Life on earth has learned to thrive in unlikely places such as boiling volcanic springs and the cold, weather-beaten rocks that rise above the surfaces of the antarctic ice cap. The atmosphere of the earth and the conditions beneath it must have changed enormously during its long history, but life went on just the same.

Not only low forms of life can make such adaptations; high forms can make them too. The highest form of animal, the mammals, thrives under conditions of both heat and cold that would kill their less well-organized rivals. The highest mammal, man, protected by his clothing, fire and mechanical contrivances, can thrive where no other animal can. This adaptability of living organisms makes it conceivable that high types of life may be thriving today on planets whose present conditions would surely prevent the appearance of primitive life.

What such creatures would look like and act like is anyone's guess. One chain of reasoning suggests that they may look surprisingly like the familiar forms on earth. An internal skeleton of hard strong material, for instance, is a fine device, and other sequences of evolution may have hit on it. A brain (that is, a communication system with a central "telephone exchange") is a necessity too, and the best place to put a brain is in a movable, well-protected member that also contains the major senses, such as the eyes, ears, and organs of smell. So the inhabitants of unknown planets may have heads and skulls of some sort. They may have legs too, for movable supports to maneuver the animal's body are convenient devices in any place where gravitation is not too powerful.

If light is available, eyes will be developed to use it as a source of information, and since the laws of optics are presumably uniform throughout the universe, the eyes of extraterrestrial races will not look very different from human eyes. They will certainly have lenses and something resembling eyelids to keep their surfaces clean.

Other theorists pooh-pooh this sort of thing as mere anthropomorphism. The form of man and other high earthside animals, they say, is the product of a long series of accidents that reach back to the fish in the primitive seas. Man has four limbs because the primitive fish had four fins, and once this pattern had been established it could not be changed readily.

Man might do better with more limbs. Elephants are a successful form, and they have kept all four of their legs while making a manipulating "hand" out of their noses. Insects make good use of all six of their legs as well as various other specialized appendages. If insects had managed to get around their limitations, chiefly their external skeleton and their inefficient breathing system, the highest animals on earth might have six legs as well as antennae and tentacles. They might have brains in the small of their backs; they might lay eggs and nurse their young through the troublesome adolescence of metamorphosis. It is too much to expect, say these free-style evolutionists, that the intelligent inhabitants of other planets should look like earthside monkeys that have recently descended from the trees. Even on the earth, very slight changes of environment during the past two billion years would have modified the long chain of evolutionary accidents and produced a final product of very different appearance.

Imagining what kind of "people" may exist on other planets of the solar system is very different from determining what kinds do exist, or if any do. As an abode for intelligent life, Mercury looks impossible except to the most persistent optimist. Venus is a mystery under its thick clouds. If its atmosphere contains a biological airsol with large scavengers prowling the dark surface below, there is no reason why some of these should not be highly intelligent. But there is no evidence of it, only a possibility.

Nearly all astronomers admit that Mars has some sort of vegetation on it, and where plants live, there must be something equivalent to animal life. Animals (organisms that eat plants) are a necessary part of the carbon cycle. Without them the plants would soon extract all the carbon dioxide from the atmosphere. Then they would have to die.

The plants on Mars are not dead. They may be as low as the lichens that grow on earthside rocks (the sunlight reflected from them seems to resemble the light reflected from lichens) but they grow each season after their fashion, and perhaps they grow rather fast.

If Mars is cursed with great dust storms, as some observers believe, its plants must grow vigorously to keep above the dust that is deposited on them. If they are still growing, there must be animals on Mars that attack their bodies and return their carbon to the atmosphere as carbon dioxide. Perhaps these animals are no bigger than earthside bacteria or fungi, which perform this function too. But they may be large, even large enough to support well-developed brains. There is no conclusive evidence on this point.

The outer planets do not look favorable to life, but astronomers know almost nothing about conditions beneath the tops of their deep atmospheres. Life may have developed on them too, in some unimaginable form. They have plenty of fluids, either gaseous or liquid or both, and enough sunlight reaches them to keep life moving. It is weak, to be sure, compared to sunlight on earth, but earthside plants can grow in very dense shade where the energy arriving from the sun is a small fraction of what it is in the open. Space explorers are entitled to hope that some kind of life exists on the outer planets.

There is a good chance that life on other planets may be in some stage of social organization. Evolution on earth has adopted the social pattern many times over in many geological ages, and it is reasonable to suppose that on other planets it has its advantages, too. The process of socialization is at least as important a part of evolution as the process of developing the bodies of individual organisms.

Each one-celled organism, whether plant or animal, has in its nucleus a group of genes which control the growth and reproduction of the rest of the cell. These genes seem to be relics of the very early stage of life when the earth was populated only by living, reproducing molecules. In the course of time they banded together in co-operating groups and gathered around them subordinate molecules that did not possess the ability of reproduction. One-celled organisms such as the protozoa are, in effect, colonies of genes which have acquired a powerful competitive advantage by working together. These cells are now the dominant form of small-scale life. The living molecules (viruses) have been reduced to the status of dependent parasites.

The next step in socialization was for the cells to form colonies of their own. They banded together to form multi-celled plants and animals which vary in size from microscopic creatures no bigger than their one-celled rivals up to sequoias and whales. They are all built of cells whose individualities have been lost in the service of the larger unit to which they belong. Human bodies are societies too: colonies of trillions of cells, all of which resemble closely the one-celled organisms that were their distant ancestors. Inside each cell are the much smaller genes: the living molecules that banded together soon after the dawn of life.

There was an excellent reason for this banding to-gether. The living molecules could grow only so large before they fetched up against limits to further increase in size. When they co-operated to form the nuclei of cells, they could grow larger and do many more things. But the cells also reached a limit eventually and were forced to co-operate too. Some of the patterns that they adopted were capable of attaining very great size, but some reached their limit soon and so had no recourse except a third stage of banding together.

About one hundred million years ago, the insects reached their size limit and did what the cells had done a billion years before. They formed large social groups with the individual insects subordinated to the welfare of the colony as a whole. These social insects (ants, wasps, bees, termites, etc.) were so successful that they have survived almost unchanged down to the present moment. There is hardly a square yard of land where life exists at all that does not contain either ants or termites. They inhabit the tropics and the temperate regions, both moist land and dry. An unprejudiced observer from another planet might well decide that the social insects are the most successful form on earth.

The socialization of the vertebrates was delayed for a long time. Their bodily pattern allowed them to grow much larger than the insects, and so they were not forced to use the device of co-operation. Their evolution tested many large experimental models (such as the dinosaurs) before it decided that mere giantism was not the path of progress. Then the evolution of the mammals, the highest type of vertebrate, abandoned giantism and turned at last to socialization. The result was man, the social mammal, who now shares control of the planet with the social insects.

The present state of things on the planet earth would be rather a puzzle to an observer from another planet. If he landed in the United States, the most conspicuous animals in sight would be automobiles, and if he examined these vigorous hard-shelled creatures, he would find that each contains one or more soft, feeble organisms that appear notably helpless when removed from their shells. He would decide, after talking with these defenseless creatures, that they have no independent existence. Few of them have anything to do with the production or transportation of food. They need clothing and shelter, but do not produce them for themselves. They are dependent on their distant fellows in thousands of complex ways. When isolated, they usually die —just like worker ants that wander helplessly and hopelessly if separated from their colony.

If the observer were intelligent (and extraterrestrial observers are always presumed to be intelligent) he would conclude that the earth is inhabited by a few very large organisms whose individual parts are subordinate to a central directing force. He might not be able to find any central brain or other controlling unit, but human biologists have the same difficulty when they try to analyze an ant hill. The individual ants are not impressive objects—in fact they are rather stupid, even for insects—but the colony as a whole behaves with striking intelligence.

When human observers descend on a foreign planet, they may find it inhabited by organisms in an even more advanced stage of social co-operation. Perhaps its moving and visible parts will be entirely secondary, like the machines of man. Perhaps the parts that are really alive will be even more helpless: mere clots of nerve tissue lying motionless and sedentary far underground. Perhaps this organic stuff, having served its creative purpose, will have withered away, leaving the machines that it has created in possession of the planet.

This state of things would not be much more extraordinary than the situation that evolution has already produced on the earth. In a sense, the cells of the human body were once independent. A few of them, the white corpuscles in the blood, retain some shreds of this independence; they wander around restlessly, acting and looking much like free-living amoebas. But most of the body's cells have lost all separateness. A higher organism has taken over, and the seat of its individuality cannot be found.

When imaginative men turn their eyes toward space and wonder whether life exists in any part of it, they may cheer themselves by remembering that life need not resemble closely the life that exists on earth. Mars looks like the only planet where life like ours could exist, and even this is doubtful. But there may be other kinds of life based on other kinds of chemistry, and they may be thriving on Venus or Jupiter. At least we cannot prove at present that they are not.

Even more interesting is the possibility that life on other planets may be in a more advanced stage of evolution. Present-day man is in a peculiar and probably fleeting stage. His individual units retain a strong sense of personality. They are, in fact, still capable under favorable circumstances of leading individual lives. But man's societies (analogous to ant colonies) are already sufficiently developed to have enormously more power and effectiveness than the individuals have.

It is not likely that this transitional situation will continue very long on the evolutionary time scale. Fifty thousand years ago man was a wild animal, living like wolves or beavers in small family groups. Fifty thousand years from now his societies may have become so close-knit that the individuals retain no sense of separate personality. Then little distinction will remain between the organic parts of the multiple organism and the in-organic parts (machines) that have been constructed by it. A million years further on—and a million years is a tick of the clock on the evolutionary time scale—man and his machines may have merged as closely as the muscles of the human body and the nerve cells that actuate them.

The explorers of space should be prepared for some such situation. If they arrive on a foreign planet when its living organisms are in an earlier stage of evolution, they may find the equivalent of dinosaurs or mollusks or even one-celled protozoa. If the planet has reached a later stage (and this is by no means impossible), it may be inhabited by a single large organism composed of many closely co-operating units.

The units may be "secondary"—machines created mil-lions of years ago by a previous form of life and given the will and ability to survive and reproduce. They may be built entirely of metals, ceramics and other du-rable materials, like man's guided missiles. If this is the case, they may be much more tolerant of their environ-ment, thriving under conditions that would destroy immediately any organism made of carbon compounds and dependent on the familiar carbon cycle.

They could live on very hot or very cold planets. They could breathe any atmosphere or none. They could build their bodies to any desirable size out of materials plentiful in their planet's crust. They could get their energy from sunlight or from nuclear reactions. Such creatures might be relics of a bygone age, many million years ago, when their planet was favorable to the origin of life, or they might be immigrants from a favored planet.

Man's space explorers are not exactly likely to find such a situation on any planet they can reach. But neither are they likely to find the equivalent of present-day man, whose semi-socialized stage of development, though interesting, can occupy only a tiny slice of evolutionary time.

22

HOME IN A VACUUM

Only one school of space-travel enthusiasts cheers itself by postulating strange kinds of life that can thrive under conditions that would make life like the earth's impossible. Another takes the view that these speculations mean little to man's space colonizers, at least for the next million years. At his present stage of evolution man cannot thrive except under conditions that are reasonably like those on earth.

Some theorists are even more pessimistic. They say that the earth is stuck with a very slummy neighborhood. None of its neighbors in the solar system, not even Mars, looks like a good prospect for real-estate development. They are not discouraged, however. They insist that the pioneers can take with them into space the atmosphere and temperature that they need to keep them comfortable.

This is what the fish, man's ancestors, did when they crawled out of the sea. They carried sea water in their veins and thus kept their tender cells bathed in the medium to which they were accustomed. Man can do the same; he can keep his individuals, the cells of his social units, bathed in earthly air even in the vacuum of space.

A good deal of thought has been invested in planning such vacuum-girt colonies. One place that invites them is the airless moon, which can be reached with comparatively little difficulty. The moon's gravitation, one-sixth of the earth's, is strong enough to supply space colonists with the necessary feeling of orientation, but it is still weak enough to facilitate greatly their labor of building the colony. The strength of solar radiation is virtually the same on the moon as it is just above the top of the earth's atmosphere. Space travelers accustomed to living in a satellite station would find it no novelty.

Constructing a favorable environment for human bodies might be easier on the moon than on a space satellite. There is no reason to suppose that all of the moon's surface is made of solid rock. It may be partly of loose material. If this is the case, the colonists can burrow deeply into it, finding an even temperature below the alternate heat and cold of the moon's surface.

They may even find water. Not much is known about the temperature of the moon's crust below its surface. If it is cold enough, water may have persisted there in liquid or frozen form. Even if no water exists on the moon as such, it can probably be extracted from the moon's rocks. Nearly all rocks on earth contain combined water that can be driven off by heating. If the colonists take with them some source of energy, either a nuclear reactor or a great mirror to concentrate the sun's radiation, they can distil water out of the moon's rocks and break it down into oxygen and hydrogen. This will remove the necessity of hauling oxygen for breathing from the distant earth.

Once the moon colony has been solidly established, the oxygen problem will be less troublesome. The colony will have a large enclosed space, perhaps a plastic dome supported by gas pressure, and inside this will operate a miniature replica of the earth's carbon cycle. The carbon dioxide produced by the breathing of the station's inhabitants will nourish plants growing rapidly in the strong sunlight. They will extract the carbon from the carbon dioxide and turn it into food materials, restoring the oxygen to the air. Then the inhabitants of the station will eat the plants, breathe the oxygen and make more carbon dioxide for the plants to utilize.

Space planners get a great deal of semi-scientific fun out of balancing the chemical economy of a bubble of synthetic atmosphere on the face of the moon. Some propose to grow the normal crop plants that produce food on earth. Others plan to use algae grown in plastic tubes full of a nutrient solution. Theoretically, at least, algae produce an enormous amount of food for a given area exposed to sunlight. The more optimistic planners believe that a rather moderate area of hydroponically grown algae will supply the colonists with both oxygen and food.

Once the colony is in operation, it can mine the metals and other minerals that are probably plentiful near the moon's surface. Then it can grow without limit, making machine tools, factories and equipment, and spreading its hydroponic gardens and artificial atmosphere over large areas of the moon's plains. There is no reason, say the planners, why a colony on the moon should not develop as rich a life as on its mother planet.

The difficulties of this sort of thing are so obvious that it is almost unkind to point them out. Even a small lunar colony would require an enormous amount of imported paraphernalia to keep its inhabitants alive. There would have to be elaborate and clever machines for doing construction work in the moon's vacuum. These would need imported spare parts and a source of energy much more manageable than a nuclear reactor. Until the artificial atmosphere had been set up and its carbon cycle established, all oxygen and food would have to be brought all the way from the earth. The effort of doing this by means of enormous shuttle rockets and an intermediate satellite station might absorb the entire energy of the human race.

But true space-travel enthusiasts vault over this obstacle by pointing to the rising curve of human power. In a few years or hundreds of years, they say, the inhabitants of the planet Earth will have enough surplus energy to set up many stations on the moon, if they choose to do so. Perhaps they will try something even more ambitious—establishing abodes for human life in space itself, with no solid footing beneath it.

True space habitations would be space ships large enough to contain all the necessary components of human culture. They would start in a modest way as satellite stations staying near the earth to draw on its resources. Eventually they would become self-sufficient, taking energy from sunlight and setting up carbon cycles to supply their inhabitants with food and oxygen. They would have rocket motors of some sort to give them maneuverability, and they could cruise at will all around the solar system.

They might, for instance, venture nearer the sun to take advantage of stronger radiation. They might circle Venus to scoop up carbon dioxide from its rich atmosphere, or they might cruise to Jupiter to take on methane and ammonia. The asteroids would be convenient sources of solid raw materials. They have virtually no gravity, and therefore the mobile space habitation could drift up to one of them and mine its nickel and iron with the greatest of ease.

Feeding on sunlight, asteroids and planetary gases, the space habitations could grow to any desirable size. They would be, in fact, mobile planets, custom-built to fit human needs. So, say the space planners, humans should thrive upon them as they never have thriven on the earth, and better kinds of men should develop quickly. So far, man has had to put up with the conditions of atmosphere, gravitation, radiation, etc., that nature provided. He may do much better under new conditions experimentally determined and artificially controlled.

The space planners point again to the ancient fish that crawled out on the land. Their modern descendants in the sea are hardly more intelligent than they were at that remote date. Fish, as fish, seem to have reached a limit, but the fish that moved to the land developed into man. Perhaps when man moves into space, he will take another step upward.

At any rate, the space habitations will not crowd one another for a long time. They can multiply almost without limit, floating in sunny space like diatoms at the surface of the sunlit ocean. Perhaps each of them will develop a characteristic culture, or specialize on manufacturing certain instruments or articles. There may be traders of space: habitations that move from orbit to orbit freighted with products or raw materials.

Perhaps if the sunlit regions close to the life-giving sun ever become crowded, or materials to build the habitations or feed their crews ever become scarce, some of them may develop into fierce carnivora, like the larger plankton organisms in a sea full of peaceful diatoms. Then evolution will have started again, close to where it began. It will repeat a second cycle, but in space instead of in the sea.

23

INTO THE BLACK YONDER

Astronauts who are not attracted by the idea of setting up housekeeping in space itself and who find the planets of the solar system dull or otherwise unsuitable are driven to canvassing the universe for pleasanter worlds to conquer. There are the stars, of course, but stars appear to be as resistant to colonization as the sun itself, which is our local star.

Less than a generation ago, nearly all astronomers would have told the space-travel enthusiasts to stop looking. The universe, they would have said, contains almost nothing but stars and such unsatisfactory stuff as interstellar dust and gas. Planetary systems were then believed to be excessively rare. Our own was supposed to have been formed when another star came near the sun and drew out of it a long filament of solar material. This gathered into planets, much as the stream from a garden hose gathers into drops.

Since the stars are extremely far apart, the chances of their colliding or grazing one another are slight. The astronomers figured that less than one star in a million could have acquired a fleet of planets in this way. Therefore they announced that the solar system must be unique or almost unique and that the intelligent life that has developed on one of its planets is probably alone in the universe. Some of the clergy cheered this conclusion. Their moral and theological rulings might be difficult to impose on bizarre inhabitants of distant worlds. So they rejoiced when the astronomers pronounced such worlds nonexistent.

Their rejoicing was premature. Modern astronomers believe that stars are formed out of clouds of cosmic gas and dust that gradually draw together over hundreds of millions or billions of years. As the mass grows more concentrated, it begins to heat up. Eventually it gets hot enough to start nuclear reactions in the deep interior of the contracting body. Then the star is really in business. Unless it blows up or otherwise behaves in an irregular manner, it can go on shining for many billion years by turning some of its hydrogen into energy, more or less after the manner of a hydrogen bomb. This is what the sun does, and the sun is an ordinary and conservative star.

During the process of star formation, planets are

likely to appear. As the gas streams inward toward the star's growing center, it is sure to take on a turbulent, whirling motion. The same thing happens in hurricanes, tornadoes, and in the little eddies that form in wash basins. The whole mass rotates, and minor eddies appear outside the main swirl. If the material in these little clots gets moving fast enough around the main mass, it never succeeds in joining it. Instead, the minor concentrations of gas and dust (known as proto-planets) settle into orbits around the growing star. Their matter gradually condenses around their own centers of gravitation, and they turn into a planetary system like our own.

The process is not catastrophic. That is, it happens normally, not because of some rare occurrence such as the contact of two stars. Since most of the stars in the sky were probably formed in this same way, they are all likely to have leftover material revolving around them in the form of planets.

This news, which trickled gradually out of the great observatories during the past generation, has cheered the space men no end. They can now look up at the sky on a clear night and assume that each speck of light is surrounded by a retinue of promising planets. They are invisible, of course. They give off no light of their own, and they are too close to their stars to be seen independently of them by weak reflected light. But when the light of certain stars is carefully measured, it fluctuates in a way that suggests that some small body is moving across the star's face. This is accepted as additional evidence that many stars have planets.

Whether these planets are habitable or not is a more complicated question. A great many stars, perhaps more than half of them, are double or triple. Some of their members revolve at enormous distances around a common center. Each of them might have planets of its own. Their inhabitants would see one star in their sky that looks a great deal brighter than any of its rivals, but there would be no other novelty in belonging to such a system.

Many double stars, however, are much closer together. Some of them revolve almost in contact with one another or may even be connected by a link of hot gaseous matter. In a few cases, small intense stars are believed to revolve inside the outer limits of large diffuse stars. Such systems would not be good mothers to a brood of life-bearing planets. Small objects revolving around either of the partners (or around both of them as a unit) would pass through periodic ordeals by fire which would probably prevent the development of life.

Other inhospitable stars are those that radiate chiefly in hard X-rays which would tear to pieces any chemicals that are trying to grow into the large, complex molecules that form the basis of life. Stars that explode periodically are unpleasant, too, and the enormous red giant stars are believed to be so young that they cannot have formed any planets. The red or white dwarfs are so old and feeble that the inhabitants of their planets, if any, must have frozen to death millions of years ago.

But after all these unsuitable stars have been eliminated, there are plenty of stars left in the sky that are placid, dependable and single like our own sun, and many of these may have bevies of contented planets. Astronomers are not greatly interested in such dull, law-abiding stars. They call them "members of the main sequence" and use them chiefly as a base for statistical studies. But astronauts cherish them, as farmers cherish a sow that is a good mother to her litter of piglets.

Another cheering factor is the recent decision by the astronomers that the composition of the universe is reasonably uniform throughout. Most stars are made chiefly of hydrogen, as the sun is, and the other elements in them are roughly in the same proportion as in the sun. So planets revolving around far-distant suns are probably made of familiar material, with metals in their cores, and oxides and silicates in their outside crusts. If they are large enough and cool enough, they will have atmospheres of familiar gases. If they have just the right size and temperature, they will have liquid oceans. Such planets may be hospitable to life, and most modern biologists believe that life will develop wherever conditions are suitable, and time has been sufficient.

When the more imaginative astronauts look at the sky, they see most of the stars as the leaders of planets that may be inhabitable, if not already inhabited. Their next step, of course, is to figure out how to visit them.

This is not easy, for as soon as a space ship leaves the solar system and heads for an alien star, it must conquer not only space but time. Even the nearer stars lie enormously far away. Their distances are measured in light years, and each light year is six trillion miles. If a space ship travels at fifty thousand miles per hour, which is a good round speed in the solar system, it will take at least thirteen thousand years of space sailing to cover a single light year. Its crew will grow old and die when the voyage has barely begun.

Space ships can be speeded up, of course, but even if they move as fast as comets whipping around the sun, they will not make appreciable progress toward any star within the lifetime of their crew.

One solution of this difficulty is nature's way—reproduction. Nature does not try to keep its higher organisms alive indefinitely. It is true that some of the lowest organisms never die unless they meet some violent end. When they prosper, they grow larger and divide in two. The parts grow and divide again. Enemies and inclement environment keep the species from multiplying too much, but none of its members dies of mere old age.

This system does not work in the higher organisms. They are too complex to split in two, and parts of them wear out, weaken or become clogged with waste or dead material. So nature's way of immortalizing a higher organism is the familiar business of sexual fertilization, gestation and birth. After having fathered or mothered a number of fresh replicas, the older individuals die. The material in their bodies returns by various routes to the common pool of chemicals out of which life is built. Thus, in spite of death, the species is immortal, just like the humble amoebae, whose individuals never grow old and die.

For a voyage to a distant star, astronauts have proposed

an interstellar breeding ship with a male and female crew. Its population, of course, will have to be controlled carefully. During long, dull periods in space when no action is expected, the crew can be permitted to become very small. Perhaps it will be predominantly female, with only a few males preserved to hold up their end of the breeding business.

Several generations before a crisis is expected, the male population can be increased, perhaps by disposing of female infants or by some means of controlling sex at conception. Then when the ship nears its objective, its crew will be large and predominantly male, with only a few young females to form the nucleus of a fast-breeding colony.

Such a Noah's Ark of space would have to be rather large, perhaps as big as a medium-sized asteroid. There has been some debate among interstellar explorers about the minimum size of a human group that can preserve its life and culture. It should not start out with a crew of trained engineers and scientists whose offspring will degenerate into barbarians before the voyage has continued more than a few generations. So the space ship will have to have room for schools, a complete university and a reference library containing all the important elements of the highest human culture.

It may be considered desirable to train some of the young people in non-technical ways. Most scientists feel a definite need for the non-taxing companionship of women with inactive minds. Besides such space houris, the crew may well include a lower caste to perform unpleasant, trivial or routine duties and be supplanted by the higher type as the ship approaches its target.

All biological material on board will have to be recycled—that is, used over and over. Carbon dioxide from the lungs of the crew will have to be separated into oxygen for rebreathing and carbon to be built into edible compounds. The bodies of the dead, of course, will be recycled and eventually eaten. If they were disposed of in any other way, such as burial in space, it would not be many generations before the ship's stock of biological material had been completely exhausted.

There should be nothing shocking about this, the astronauts point out quickly. It is exactly what happens on earth, which is a large space ship with a closed biological system. The bodies of people alive today are made of material that has been recycled many times.

All this sounds rather difficult, and the astronauts admit that it may be unpleasant for the crew. But if all goes well on the Noah's Ark traveling through space at fifty thousand miles per hour, its 146,000th generation can colonize the Pleiades.

To lessen the tedium of the long dull voyages, some of the proponents of the Noah's Ark method favor putting most of the crew into a state of suspended animation. A few will stay awake for specified tours of duty, watching over their shipmates, who lie insensible, perhaps in refrigerated and sealed compartments. It may be possible to put the whole crew to sleep in this way and provide some kind of alarm clock to wake them up when their destination has drawn near, or when danger threatens.

A space ship of this sort would be like the spore of a fungus, which can drift through the air indefinitely, as lifeless to all appearances as a mineral particle. But when a spore alights on a suitable surface, say a juicy plant tissue or a rotten stump, its suspended life awakens and quickly generates a network of hungry white threads.

In the same way the silent space ship, loaded with its genetic material of human life and culture, will drift for thousands of millions of years through the empty reaches of interstellar space. When it approaches a star that has suitable planets, its alarm bells will rouse the inhabitants to complex and vigorous action. Its packed machinery will come to life; its telescopes will peer ahead; its rocket motors will roar. When it reaches the selected planet, a fierce task force of men and machines will be ready to sally out and take possession of it.

The Noah's Ark method is not admired by all the interstellar space men. They consider it unimaginative, and they believe that they know a better way—telescoping time by means of relativity. When any object, including a space ship, moves at nearly the speed of light, its time slows down. It can sail like a cosmic ray for thousands or hundreds of thousands of earth years from star to star, but if its speed comes close enough to the speed of light, its crew will feel that only a few weeks have passed.

A great deal of high-level mathematical thought has been expended on this problem, and the figuring has become both complex and controversial. There is no doubt, however, about the dilation of time with speed; it has actually been checked experimentally.

The short-lived particles called *mu* mesons that are created by cosmic rays in the high atmosphere are known to have a normal life of about two-millionths of a second. They are formed on the average about ten miles above the earth's surface. So even if they were traveling at the speed of light itself, they should not be able to reach the ground in their brief lifetimes. The fact is that a great many of them do reach the surface and are detected there by man's instruments. This is interpreted to mean that the speed of the *mu* mesons, which is only a tiny fraction less than the speed of light, has made their time slow down, permitting them to live long enough to reach the surface of the earth.

Taking off happily from this point, the interstellar voyagers propose to make their space ships fly by some unspecified means almost as fast as the *mu* mesons. To use the calculations of L. R. Shepherd, Ph.D., of Cambridge, writing in the *Journal* of the British Interplanetary Society, a space ship traveling with 99 per cent of the speed of light could make the round trip to the star Procyon (which is 10.4 light years away) in 21 years. But this is the passage of time recorded by the space ship's sponsors who have stayed behind on the earth. Its crew would be convinced that they had been traveling for only three years. A closer approach to the speed of light would let them reach even more distant stars in even less personal time.

They might have trouble, of course, with the very thin gas that exists between the stars. Though its molecules might be at rest, they would hit the space ship at close to the speed of light and they would act on it like the dangerous beams of particles that are shot out of high-power cyclotrons. They would penetrate its skin like bullets shot into butter, and their effect on human tissue would not be good.

Another trouble with the time dilation system is that the voyagers would say good-bye forever to the friends, perhaps even to the civilization, that they left behind on earth. If they return safely and still reasonably young from a journey covering 2,000 light years of distance, they will find that their friends have receded into ancient history, and perhaps that the name of the nation that sent them out into space has been almost forgotten. This prospect troubles the would-be interstellar explorers, who do not relish becoming Rip Van Winkles of space.

Another objection, less picturesque, is raised by mathematicians who claim that the voyagers would gain time through speed on the outward trip, but would lose an equal amount of time on the return journey. It takes a highly skilled mathematician to argue this point, and most of the interstellar planners believe that it has been settled in their favor.

For astronauts who want to explore the really distant stars, like those on the other side of the Milky Way Galaxy, the relativistic time-dilation method is too slow. Relativity teaches that nothing (nothing at all) can travel faster than light, and it takes light 100,000 years to reach the far side of the galaxy, even if it does not have to detour around the mysterious, star-packed and presumably dangerous nucleus. For voyages to other galaxies, most of which lie millions of light years away, the speed of light is completely inadequate. On the intergalactic scale, light travels as slowly as an amoeba crawling in a film of water.

So the ultimate astronauts, the intergalactic travelers, take refuge in those branches of higher mathematics that deal with space that has more than three dimensions. They propose to find means of entering the fourth dimension and using it as a short cut for reaching distant objects.

The best way to visualize this convenient device is to imagine two-dimensional people. Their universe is a surface like that of a sheet of paper. Everything that does not lie exactly on this surface has no existence for them. They can form no conception of three-dimensional objects, or of space that lies off the thin plane of their world. If the paper that they live on were to be bent in a near circle, they could not cut across from one edge to the other. They could conceive of no possible route except the long way around the circle of paper.

Men are three-dimensional and live in a three-dimensional world. Except by calling time the fourth dimension (which is not exactly playing fair), they cannot imagine a four-dimensional world. But who knows? It may exist all around them, even inside them, and their limited three-dimensional world may be bent in a circle like a sheet of paper.

This thought encourages the intergalactic travelers. The most distant galaxies, which look like faint smudges of light even in the photographs of the Palomar Mountain telescope, may be just around the corner in four-dimensional space. If this is so, say the intergalactic astronauts, the thing to do is to develop some new understanding which will enable three-dimensional men to build a vehicle that can navigate the fourth dimension. It will vanish from sight, apparently from existence, and pop up quickly in a foreign galaxy billions of light years away.

24

LEADING IMAGINATION

Upon such theories, which still have a flavor of science about them if they are not taken too seriously, the entertaining structure of space fiction has been constructed. While the conservative space men are still planning how to get off the earth and the moderate radicals are messing around in the solar system, the space fictioneers are cruising the whole universe, using what they call "time shift" (relativistic time dilation) and "space warp" (the fourth-dimension trick) to cover inconvenient distances. In some galaxy or other they can find any kind of planet they want, and almost always it is inhabited by exceptionally beautiful women. They may have hydrochloric acid running in their veins, and the language they speak may be based on symbolic logic, but it is a convention of space fiction that they are sexually attractive in a familiar, if somewhat souped-up way.

A large public does not distinguish between space fact and space fiction, apparently believing that travel to the planets of distant stars is just as imminent as flight to a nearby orbit around the familiar earth. Most practical rocket men read space fiction and some of them think it arouses a desirable popular interest. Others are not so sure. "What these space fans are expecting," said one of them recently, "is intergalactic flying saucers that take off after breakfast, easy like helicopters, and land in the Whirlpool Galaxy in time for the cocktail hour. Why should they get excited about our measly rockets that can't even fly to the moon?"

The practical rocket men fear that their gradual march toward space, spotted with heartbreaking setbacks, would disappoint the oversold public, even if military secrecy were relaxed enough to permit them to crow about every small triumph. They also fear that the space-fiction cosmos of fantasy, with its beautiful, wise and Christlike super-insects and its invisibility, immortality and freedom from all other limiting parameters, will make exploration of the solar system seem hardly worthwhile. But rocket men who have some knowledge of human cultural history (and a surprising number of them do) comfort themselves by citing the swarming travelers' tales of the age before Columbus.

The small sickly benighted world of medieval Europe was surrounded on all sides by glittering realms of fantasy. A many-storied Heaven floated in the sky above it, and many sub-basements of Hell smoked and rumbled below. The levels of the heavenly sector were peopled with angels and saints, cherubim and seraphim, and the souls of the saved. The basements and sub-basements were swarming with devils and witches, gigantic bats and fire-breathing dragons. In other crannies of the medieval mind lived basilisks and werewolves, cobalts and leprechauns. These diverse places and beings were intensely real. Belief in many of them was officially encouraged by the clergy, if not officially enforced. People who accepted such notions, as many did, could wander through environments just as fantastic as any discovered on distant galaxies by modern space-fiction writers.

This riot of pure superstition did not keep medieval Europeans from taking intense interest in tales on a lower and more realistic level. News of a sort seeped in from the outside world. Occasional travelers returned with reports of Eastern cultures far more advanced and interesting than those of backward Europe. The fantasy tales from the lands of the infidels penetrated Europe under their own power. Flying carpets (the flying saucers of Islam) were convenient vehicles for a kind of exploration. Sometimes they brought accounts of real but far distant lands that Europeans could not reach.

It was hard for Europeans to distinguish between stories about Heaven and Hell, literary fantasies of valleys floored with diamonds, and real factual reporting such as the description by Marco Polo of the court of Kublai Khan. Most Europeans made little distinction, accepting the whole mixed bag as equally real and entertaining.

When Western Europeans finally awoke from their long coma and began to penetrate beyond the narrow boundaries that had surrounded them for centuries, they searched for the things and places that they had heard about in the fantasy tales. Ambassadors were sent by the Pope to the Court of Prester John, which had never existed. Cities paved with gold were searched for over each beckoning horizon. Explorers sought Lands of the Blessed, countries of warrior women and fountains of youth. They found no such things, of course, but the things they did find outside little Europe proved as interesting and exciting as the tales that had drawn them into the unknown.

As their technical skill increased with the growing freedom of their minds, they found that places like North America, the jungles of Africa, and the steppes of Russia, which had looked like forbidding wildernesses, were full of treasures more valuable than any gold-paved city. In some of these places, and with the aid of their products, were constructed vigorous new societies.

The more realistic explorers of space take comfort from this precedent. Europeans were properly delighted when they discovered even the small but real Azores. They made good use of forbidding New England, and they dug more diamonds in South Africa than Sinbad the Sailor had found in his valley full of snakes. They did not find the Fountain of Youth, but the scientific age that began when Europeans broke out of their prison of superstition has abolished most of the diseases that killed the majority of pre-scientific men before they had left childhood. This is better in many ways than perpetuating youth.

In the same manner, the space-travel enthusiasts hope, their slow and difficult penetration beyond the boundaries of the earth will not seem too much of an anticlimax to the gaudy fantasies of space fiction.

When the proponents of space flight try to work out a practical procedure to urge on the public, they fall into violent disagreement. Those who follow the prophet von Braun believe that a "crash" program is absolutely necessary. In their opinion, the comparatively conservative designers of military guided missiles will never reach space by the careful procedure that they are following today. Their little-by-little plodding is not sufficiently inspiring. It is too much like other military engineering, which has always been notorious for its lack of imagination. It does not attract the class of men who staffed the American atom-bomb project and the V-2 development in Germany.

Both of these were crash programs that worked in an atmosphere of excitement and hope. Both of them had great goals which numerous critics considered unattainable. Both spent large amounts of time and money on items that did not succeed, but both were brilliantly successful in reaching their ultimate objectives. Von Braun believes that if either of them had inched along with careful, prudent steps, it would never have reached its first base.

The present United States missile program, von Braun believes, is proceeding much too prudently. He thinks that it will prove insufficient even in a strictly military sense. The security of the free world, in his opinion, has depended since the end of the war on the long-range strategic airplane carrying atom bombs. This preventive weapon has almost played out. The Russians will soon have ground-to-air guided missiles that can knock down any ponderous bomber that invades their skies. Making the bombers fly faster will not do much good. The guided missiles can be made to fly faster, too.

Von Braun has a low opinion of strategic guided missiles that will strike at the heart of the Soviet Union from bases outside its boundaries. They will be a step in advance, he says, but the Russians will copy them promptly or develop them for themselves. Missiles that stay near the earth offer no permanent supremacy to the free world. All they offer is a means for both sides to destroy each other quickly.

But, says von Braun, the atom-armed space station with its all-seeing telescopic eyes is in an entirely different category. The first nation or group of nations that fortifies and arms an orbit can control the whole earth permanently. Its bristling, invulnerable satellites cannot be attacked successfully or copied in secret. Preparations by the Soviet Union to send any vehicle into space can be detected and destroyed in their early stages. The artificial moons, flying the flags of the free world in airless space, will keep the peace on pain of destruction, and do so as long as the human race finds such policing necessary. At last, when war has been relegated to the status of murder, the satellites will serve as bases for the spread of the human species beyond the little planet where it originated.

To establish satellites, says von Braun, will not cost more than four billion dollars. This is only one-tenth of what the United States is spending each year on its military establishments. If spread over ten years in chunks of four hundred million dollars each, the cost of the satellites will hardly be noticed. It will be far down the list of military procurement, not much above the cost of many useless military "'empires" constructed by the Pentagon to give employment to high-ranking officers.

The practical objections to von Braun's crash program have been given in as much detail as military secrecy permits. A more bitter criticism attacks von Braun's sincerity. "Look at this von Braun," says one of his most violent critics. "He is the man who lost the war for Hitler. His V-2 was a great engineering achievement, but it had almost no military effect, and it drained German brains and material from more practical weapons. Von Braun has always wanted to be the Columbus of space. He was thinking of space flight, not weapons, when he sold the V-2 to Hitler. He says so himself. He is still thinking of space flight, not weapons, and he is trying to sell the United States a space-flight project disguised as a means of dominating the world."

Not all historians of military history agree with this estimate of the V-2's effectiveness, but some observers on the spot are even more emphatic. In 1945, a German-speaking United States Army officer, who now works at White Sands, was sent to collapsing Germany to gather technical information. He penetrated the chaos of the dissolving battlefronts and reached the fabulous underground factory at Nordhausen where the V-2s were assembled. The director of the place was still in his bomb-proof office. He broke down and wept when he talked of the V-2s. "For each V-2," he said, "we Germans could have built at least one jet interceptor, and each would have shot down at least one of your bombers that have destroyed our country."

This history will be repeated, warn the practical missile men, if Pentagon empire-building or plain reckless enthusiasm gives von Braun and his associates the money and men for their crash-program satellite. It will almost certainly fail, and even if it does succeed, it will not give the United States the promised military advantage. Meanwhile, the United States guided-missile program, starved for money and brains, will wither to nothing. In due course Russian missiles will strike down out of space to obliterate United States targets. Then some American industrialist will tell a commissar a story like the one that was told, with tears, by the director of Nordhausen.

Von Braun smiles at these dark forebodings and dismisses his critics as men of little faith. Space flight will come, he says, and the first satellite parked in its orbit had better carry American markings and be accompanied by American atom-armed missiles. The satellite idea is not a secret; neither are most of the technical principles that are needed to put one in its orbit. If Americans do not launch a satellite, he says, the Russians will do so eventually unless they have some other scheme for controlling the earth.

This debate between von Braun and his critics could go on interminably. It does go on, both publicly and in secret, and it will go on for years. It involves that familiar military problem of how great a project to undertake in order to have the most powerful weapon at the moment when weapons are needed. On one point, von Braun and nearly all of the missile and rocket experts are agreed completely: that space flight is inevitable and that it is the next great step in human evolution. If it does not come in ten years, then it will come in fifty or one hundred years. The human race has only begun to feel the thrill of its power.

25

RISING CURVES

The philosophers of technology are fond of drawing curves to represent the rate of change in human culture. Nearly all the curves they draw turn out exponential, rising ever more steeply like the curve of squares (1, 4, 9, 16, 25, 36, 49 . . .). Each figure is not only larger than its predecessor but exceeds it by a greater amount.

There are many such steepening curves in modern human affairs. One, as we have seen, is the number of young men who can be freed from production for higher training of their brains. Another is the power demanded by industry. Another, less definite but more important, is the amount of change brought about by science in the lives of ordinary people.

There has been more change in the past ten years than in the previous fifty, and more change in that fifty years than in the previous two hundred. If this key curve continues to sweep upward, as it shows every sign of doing, the changes will come faster and faster with no end in sight.

The most sweeping curve of all traces the rate of evolution of the human race. Julian Huxley points out in his extraordinary book, *Evolution in Action,* that the development of the species is exponential too. Until very recently, he says, evolution progressed only by making bodily changes in its organisms. Fish grew lungs and legs and so could live on land. Mammals developed means of controlling their body temperatures, and thus gained a long list of important advantages. The higher mammals acquired brains that enabled them to think after a fashion, and outthink the species that were their competitors. Each of these major improvements was the sum of many small ones, and every step in advance took an enormous amount of time, measured in millions of years.

One small group of mammals explored the possible advantages of developing very large brains. Step by step, over geological ages, the humanoid apes became more and more intelligent until their ability to use primitive tools and weapons and to make simple plans enabled them to compete successfully with physically superior rivals.

These humanoids at last became men in the physical sense. Anthropologists do not know whether their skins were white or brown or black or what kind of hair they had, but they are sure that they would not attract attention in a modern city crowd if dressed in modern fashion. There was a deep difference, however: the pre-men were still animals. Their brains might be as big or almost as big as those of true humans, but they behaved like animals, and for half a million years they remained rare and weak, a marginal genus on the edge of the stream of life.

The turning point came not through physical improvement (there has been little change) but through an intellectual tool: effective speech. Anthropologists do not know how men learned to talk. The development of speech may have taken a long time, involving some changes in the brain's organization. It may have come about quickly. At any rate, the ability to talk had a magical effect on the fortunes of the highest primates.

It allowed them to accumulate group experience. Among speechless animals this is impossible; the lifetime experience of each individual dies when he does. The young can learn only by example, as young wolves learn to hunt by watching their elders. But as soon as men could talk, the adults could give the young the full benefit of their experience. They could tell the teen-agers, for instance, what to do about a bear met by chance in a cave. They did not need an actual bear (a dangerous exhibit) to illustrate their lectures. They had a word for "bear" and for tactics to be used against it.

Groups of men armed with speech soon accumulated bodies of experience far more extensive and useful than any single man could acquire for himself in his lifetime. When a group happened to contain a man who discovered something new, his superior knowledge did not die when he did. It remained a part of the group's common knowledge and was used by all members long after he was gone.

Huxley points out that a group whose members can hand down knowledge across the generations is no longer dependent on the slow processes of physical evolution. Without any bodily change in its individuals, it can grow in ability to defeat its enemies and exploit its environment. A small discovery by a single individual, say an improvement in making spearheads, quickly benefits the group as a whole and eventually passes beyond its boundaries to benefit the whole species. A few such discoveries may make the difference between extinction and survival.

Anthropologists cannot set a date when man's physical evolution was outpaced by the evolution of his social groups. In favorable places at least, the new system of pooling and accumulating knowledge brought extremely rapid development. It permitted mankind, which had changed hardly at all for several hundred thousand years, to blossom out with complex cultures in a few thousand years. Then came a rush of great inventions—agriculture, writing, metalworking—that enabled the human race to defeat permanently all the competing organisms that had evolved on his planet.

Physical evolution, says Huxley, is now of little importance. The lower animals are evolving as before, but their slow rate of improvement is leaving them hopelessly behind. Man's evolution—which is social, not physical—is moving with flashing speed from triumph to triumph. During the three hundred years since the firm establishment of scientific thinking, man has gained more power than during the seven thousand years since the discovery of agriculture. It is not too much to expect that the next hundred years will bring changes more profound than those that have taken place since neolithic times.

When the would-be conquerors of space contemplate these curves, all of them sweeping upward at an eversteepening angle, they feel great confidence. All they need do, they say, is to wait for a little while until the booming human race has acquired enough power to spread beyond its first planet. Julian Huxley himself seems to feel this way. In his book he does not discuss space exploration, but he says that man's system of accumulating knowledge has already made him an important factor in the affairs of the universe.

There is some uncertainty, of course, in all attempts to extrapolate curves beyond their present position. No matter how steeply a curve is rising, it may be approaching a point where it will level off, or even turn down.

A number of things can check the headlong evolution of human society. In the words of Robert Oppenheimer, the human race already possesses the means (atomic energy) "to commit suicide at will." Perhaps it will blow its own brains out, or even make the earth uninhabitable. This is not possible with existing stocks of atomic bombs, but the production rate of fissionable material is another ever-steepening curve.

A second kind of setback can come from an authoritarian world government (not necessarily Communist) that tries to keep its hierarchy in power by checking scientific research, which always leads to change. Or perhaps all human cultures, including our own, grow old and die because of weaknesses that lie deeply hidden until they have taken effect.

Some space-travel enthusiasts admit that a serious setback of one of these kinds might keep the race on the earth another thousand years. Others are sure that nothing can do it. A few more steps in human development, and the steps come closer and closer, will send man's space ships cruising among the planets and mapping them as sites for colonies.

Such high-altitude thinking has little to do with the short-term tactics of space flight: the unsolved problem of getting off the earth at all. The Prophet of Space, Dr. Wernher von Braun, believes that the only way to do it is for the United States, starting immediately, to make an all-out effort to establish a full-blown satellite in an orbit around the earth. The practical missile men believe that space can be conquered more surely and with less effort by slow and careful stages.

Most of them agree that it is possible at present to build a rocket, probably of three stages and not very large, which will land a small payload on the moon. It might do no more than explode a charge of flash powder that can be seen as a spark of light against the dark surface, or it might spread carbon black or other dense pigment that will make a permanent splotch on one of the moon's plains. Since the moon has no atmosphere, an explosive charge would spread such a powder widely.

When control methods improve a little, a missile might be sent to circumnavigate the moon. This will require accurate aiming, for the moon's gravitational field is small, and the missile will have to hit exactly the right part of it. The passage will presumably be made when the far side of the moon is in sunlight, so that cameras can report what they have seen there.

The next step will be to land on the moon a small unmanned observation station to look around it with television eyes, feel the ground for seismic tremors and analyze the moon's dusty "soils." Its reports can return to earth over radio channels. It might be equipped electronically so that it can be "called up" from earth and questioned from time to time.

Experience gained in this way will eventually lead to a man-carrying rocket that can ascend into space, stay there for a while, and return without killing its passengers. Once this has been done it will be comparatively easy to place manned satellites in an orbit. Then the nearer planets will not be safe from intruders for long.

No one is in a position to guess at a timetable for such a program. The key engineering facts are covered by military secrecy, and they are so widely scattered among isolated groups of missile experts that no single man knows half of them. To make a reasonably accurate estimate he would have to combine the latest news about fuels and their production, about the theory of combustion, about propulsion equipment, about control systems, electronic brains, high-altitude meteorology and space medicine.

Von Braun and his critics agree about what should be done to clear up this uncertainty. The United States Government, they say, should gather a commission of top-flight scientists to study the whole question. Its members should be cleared for all military secrets, and they should be above both Pentagon politics and the commercial lobbying of airplane or missile manufacturers. A commission of this sort, which would not be expensive, would be able to draw up a timetable for the first steps of expansion into space.

The general public, of course, would not hear the commission's decision for many years. Its report would reveal, among other things, the practical feasibility of controlling the earth militarily from an armed satellite. To publish it would give the Russians the benefit of American experience. If favorable, it might stimulate them to a furious effort to send up a satellite of their own. If unfavorable, it might save them from wasting their substance on a project doomed to failure.

With the world in its present untrusting state of mind, the public must be reconciled to seeing the first triumphs of space flight as accomplished facts. The almost total secrecy that surrounded the wartime atom-bomb project proved that programs touching a large part of the nation can be carried through to success without the public's hearing more than vague rumors about them. So if the commission is set up (it may have been set up already) and if it makes a favorable report (it may have done so already), a satellite may appear in the sky a few years hence as unheralded as a comet streaking in from space.

Perhaps the initial effort will be less ambitious. Von Braun, who is capable, with an effort, of making small plans as well as big ones, is sure that even slight extensions of present missile techniques can set a small, unmanned rocket circling in an orbit just outside the atmosphere. It can send back valuable information by telemetering, and its very existence will be a warning to international troublemakers.

When von Braun was working on rockets in Germany, he once fired a V-2 soon after sunset on a very clear day. The surface of the earth was already in darkness, and the stars were coming out. As the great rocket climbed upward, the flame of its exhaust diminished to a shining pinpoint and disappeared.

Then, after an interval, the rocket broke into the sunlight above the shadow of the earth, where it gleamed, brilliantly visible, against the darkening sky. Von Braun and all of Peenemünde watched it enchanted. They cheered as it rose like a bright, climbing star, and sorrowed to see it fall down again into the shadow.

Even a small rocket, says von Braun, can be made to shine at dusk against the dark sky. Once established in its orbit, it will inflate a white plastic balloon 100 feet in diameter. Swinging swiftly around the earth 200 miles above the surface, the balloon will gleam as brightly in the sunlight as a first-magnitude star. Von Braun believes that this "American star" rising in the West will make an enormous impression on the peoples of Asia. It will not be difficult to do this, he pleads, and will not cost much.

There are men with influence who favor such a project, and many more who would like to. So perhaps— and the key word in space flight is obstinately "perhaps" —the first small achievement of the space men will be an American star rising in the West.

INDEX

ABOUT THE AUTHOR

Jonathan Norton Leonard is a native of Sandwich, Massachusetts, on Cape Cod, and a graduate of Harvard, where he specialized in chemistry. He has been a professional writer all his working life, covering the field from *Saturday Evening Post* fiction, sometimes with a scientific angle, to books on science and technology. His books are *Loki: The Life of Charles Proteus Steinmetz, Crusaders of Chemistry, The Tragedy of Henry Ford, Men of Maracaibo, Three Years Down, Tools of Tomorrow,* and *Enjoyment of Science.*

For seven years Mr. Leonard has been science editor of *Time* magazine, a position that keeps him in touch with the advancing frontier of science. In the course of his regular work he has watched the detonations of atomic bombs, the flights of rockets and the silent "thinking" of electronic computers. He has flown in jet planes, looked at the stars through famous telescopes, visited hundreds of laboratories and talked with thousands of scientists. "For me," he says, "this is the most interesting job in the world. No kind of fiction could be as exciting as real science is."